TEACH YOURSELF BOOKS

THE SLIDE RULE

D1479197

This book aims to increase the popularity of the Slide Rule. It is hoped that it may help to remove the fallacy that there is something difficult or even mysterious connected with a simple instrument with which everybody who has calculations to make should be acquainted. Clear, fully illustrated explanations are given of different slide rule systems, simple and complex, and how they are used. For the beginner and the specialist who wishes to bring his knowledge up-to-date this is a valuable book.

"As the Arabs Say . . ."

TEACH YOURSELF BOOKS

THE SLIDE RULE

BURNS SNODGRASS,
M.B.E., A.R.C.Sc.

TEACH YOURSELF BOOKS

ST. PAUL'S HOUSE WARWICK LANE LONDON EC4

First printed 1955
Revised edition 1971
2nd impression 1972

Revised Edition Copyright © 1971
The English Universities Press Limited

ISBN 0 340 15368 7

Printed in Great Britain for The English Universities Press Ltd. by T. and A. Constable Ltd., Hopetoun Street, Edinburgh

CONTENTS

FOREWORD

THE present era is sometimes termed the mechanical age because so many operations which, in earlier days, were carried out slowly and often painfully by hand are now performed by machines with an enormous saving in time and effort.

The slide rule cannot be regarded as a modern invention since the first design dates from the early part of the seventeenth century, but every year sees additions and variations made and the up-to-date instrument has, as might be expected, advanced greatly beyond the earlier types. Every year a considerable number of Patent Specifications are lodged in the British Patents Office to give protection to the latest inventions in slide rule technique, and we may say fairly that the slide rule in its own field is keeping pace with modern mechanical advance.

This Teach Yourself Book is published to increase the popularity of the slide rule. It is hoped that it may help to remove the fallacy that there is something difficult or even mysterious connected with a simple instrument with which everybody who has calculations to make should be acquainted.

Among the technicians and artisans upon whom we so much depend for the maintenance and improvement of national prosperity are many who have frequently to make calculations. They would be hampered in their activities if the improvements we have referred to had not extended to expediting their work. The slide rule and other instruments which give the same facilities for rapid calculations are covered by the term "Mechanical Calculation".

It is unfortunate that, for some reasons not easy to see, the slide rule is sometimes regarded as a difficult instrument with which to become proficient. There is a tendency for some people to become facetious in their references to this simple instrument. Journalists and broadcasters are great offenders in this respect, and some of their references are unbelievably absurd and show a lack of elementary knowledge.

The clumsy and unscientific systems of monetary units and measurements of weight, length and area which have grown up all over the world can be handled with some small difficulty by slide rule calculations. However, with the rapid change to the decimal system of measurement into which, in most cases, the slide rule is divided, even this problem is rapidly vanishing.

We have said that, in general, slide rule scales are subdivided in decimal fractions and, since there are still some people who cannot easily calculate in the decimal system, we give at an early stage a simple explanation of the principles of this system. Perhaps we need hardly add that any sections of this book which deal with matters with which the reader is quite familiar may be glanced at and passed over.

We shall find that the underlying principle of the slide rule is calculation by logarithms. Just as a man may be an expert motor-car driver without understanding the principles of the internal-combustion engine and the mechanism of his car, so can a slide rule be used without the slightest knowledge of logarithms. In fact, we hesitated at including the section on logarithms in case the mention of the term might cause discouragement and increase the sense of awe with which some people regard the slide rule. The section on logarithms may be disregarded entirely, and indeed we ask that it should be, on the first reading of this book, but when the rudiments of the slide rule have been mastered—and again we stress the simplicity of these—it may be that some readers will find interest and advantage in learning something of the first principles of "logs"—one of the most fascinating parts of elementary mathematics.

Another factor which has contributed to the reluctance of people to purchase a slide rule lies in the erroneous impression that it is a costly instrument. Naturally enough, people are averse to paying two or three pounds for an instrument which they fear may be of little use to them. Inexpensive slide rules have been available in this country for over thirty years, and their makers claim that for accuracy and utility they are equal to the more expensive varieties which have been manufactured for a much longer period. The first "Unique" slide rule, the 10″ log-log model, was produced at a popular price for students. Its introduction was welcomed, and it met with success. There are now about a score of different slide rules in the "Unique" range, and sales have progressively increased, and it may fairly be said that this make of rule is now the "best seller" in this country. "Unique" slide rules carry all the useful scales, including the log-log scale, in most models. In the expensive type of rule the inclusion of the log-log scale means a much higher-priced instrument than the "standard" or ordinary models. The log-log scale in the "Unique" range is included at no increase in the cost of the rule. The makers of "Unique" slide rules introduced a new technique in manufacture by printing the scales and coating them with transparent plastic material. This important change allowed of a great reduction in the manufacturing cost as compared with the older method of separately dividing the scales.

This book, however, is not published primarily to boost any particular make of slide rule. All slide rules are difficult to manufacture, and in most cases are honestly worth the prices charged for them. Some shopkeepers charge more than the recognised retail prices fixed by the manufacturers, and purchasers should be vigilant and resist any attempt at this sort of imposition.

We would, with all respect, urge members of the teaching profession to make more effective efforts to introduce the slide rule into schools. The proper place to become acquainted with this invaluable time-saver is in the classrooms of the primary schools; normal boys and girls of the age of 13 or 14 years are able to attain proficiency in its use. More often than not the student does not become acquainted with the slide rule until he or she reaches a technical school or college, and even in such institutions the slide rule is by no means the universal and everyday instrument it deserves to be.

The writer has had long experience of teaching in a technical college and has never had the least difficulty in arousing interest in the application of the slide rule to practical problems.

There was never any necessity to urge students to adopt the rule; directly a slide rule appeared in a classroom and was demonstrated, students expressed the desire to acquire one, and within a week or two the majority had done so. A few minutes devoted to insttirucon were sufficient to teach the fundamentals. We know that the slide rule is used in a number of primary and central schools by teachers who think as we do. Unfortunately, we also know that even in some grammar and secondary schools a slide rule is almost unknown.

We hope we shall not be accused of unduly stressing the advantage of slide rules which depart from the standard type. We can only attribute to the conservatism with which most of us are endowed the fact that the large majority of slide rules in use are of the standard type whose salient features are the A, B, C and D scales. Men who have used a slide rule for years have never handled any other than the standard type; to them we would suggest a change to a more efficient instrument, several of which we mention later. The standard type slide rule, except for the beginner, is moribund.

For the tyro we advise first the reading of Sections 1 and 3, making sure he can read the scales, He should read also Section 2 if he is likely to have any difficulty with decimals.

He should then *study* Section 4 thoroughly, since this is the most important part of the early instruction. This section deals with C and D scales, which are by far the most used scales of the standard slide rule.

He should use his slide rule for the examples and problems given in the text and work through additional simple examples he can make up for himself, using numbers which can be easily reduced mentally. Such examples as $\dfrac{6 \times 9 \times 16}{2 \times 4}$, which gives 108 as the result. He may say that it is not worth while using a slide rule to calculate a result he can obtain mentally, and he would be quite right, but we are here advising how to approach the slide rule and to gain experience and confidence in using it.

The student may then use these figures $\dfrac{6 \cdot 42 \times 9 \cdot 35 \times 16 \cdot 7}{2 \cdot 04 \times 4 \cdot 41}$,

كما قالت العرب

"As the Arabs Say . . ."

Arabic Quotations Recalled and Interpreted
by Isa Khalil Sabbagh

Library of Congress Catalog Card Number
83-090108

ISBN 0-912369-00-0

First Edition

which he cannot cope with mentally. He should obtain as a result 111·5 and he will see how the position of decimal point has been fixed.

For the experienced reader we recommend the dualistic slide rule as being the best available for general purposes. This rule is discussed in Section 10. It is quicker in action, more accurate in its results and the irritating necessity of traversing the slide when using the more usual type of slide rule is eliminated.

We include in the explanatory sections of the book examples in respect of which the movements of slide and cursor are indicated. Often there are alternative ways of selecting various factors, giving rise to alternative ways of moving the slide and cursor. For practice some of these should be worked out by the reader.

Problems are inserted for the student to solve, and a check can be made by comparing results with those given at the end of the book. To reduce typography in the worked examples, abbreviations are used; these are mentioned in Section 4.

THE PRINCIPLE OF THE SLIDE RULE

THE reader will agree that the arithmetical operations of addition and subtraction are less tedious to carry out than those of multiplication and division. When very simple numbers are involved, none of these four operations gives trouble, and it is just as simple to multiply 4 by 2 as to add together 4 and 2. When the numbers are larger, this is no longer the case. It is still comparatively easy to add together, say, 492 and 374; most people could perform the operation mentally, and give the result as 866, without resorting to the aid of pencil and paper. If, however, these two numbers have to be multiplied together, only a few people who have the unusual gift of being able to cope with such computations mentally could give the answer with confidence. As a test of memory and concentration write down these numbers with a view to multiplication, namely,

$$374$$
$$492$$
$$\overline{}$$

now lay down your pencil and try to complete the multiplication, memorising the figures as they emerge, and then mentally add up the three resulting lines. It is clear that to obtain a correct result one must possess exceptional powers; in fact, to perform mentally the operations correctly with two figure factors is commendable. Addition or subtraction remain comparatively simple, and can be quickly performed with even a dozen or any number of factors, but multiplication and division when carried out by ordinary arithmetical means become progressively more tedious as the number of factors increases.

There are now in use, for office and industrial purposes, ingenious calculating machines. These are, comparatively, of recent origin, and are designed to deal rapidly with the masses of routine computations which have to be dealt with in large offices, banks and industrial organisations. For their particular purposes they stand supreme, and it is no part of this treatise to deal with them. To some extent these elaborate and expensive machines execute the same operations as the simple slide rule, but many operations which can be effected by slide rule are impossible with the calculating machine, and the converse applies also.

Reverting to our simple addition of 4 and 2, it is clear that we could perform the operation with the use of two scales placed as shown in Fig. 1. These scales might be divided in any arbitrary unit, and if each unit was subdivided into tenths we could effect the addition of such quantities as $3 \cdot 6 + 7 \cdot 8$.

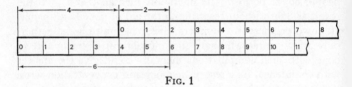

FIG. 1

Further, if we had a convenient way of marking the result of the first addition by means of an index sliding along the lower scale, we could proceed to add or subtract as many factors as we desired. The reader will have no difficulty in seeing how subtraction would be effected, and he need not be much concerned at the possibility of requiring an absurdly long lower scale; since we are not suggesting that anyone would indulge in this unpracticable demonstration, we are leading up to the slide rule method of multiplication.

Now please examine the scales indicated in Fig. 2. You will first notice that while the end divisions are marked 0 in Fig. 1 they are marked 1 in Fig. 2. You will also observe that, whereas in Fig. 1 the graduations are marked 0, 1, 2, 3, etc., in Fig. 2 they are marked 1, 2, 4, 8, 16, etc., each number being twice the value of the preceding one. Clearly, if all the graduations were shown in Fig. 2, there would be a great crowding together

Dedication

To my late father, from whom I inherited this passion
for quotations;

To my dear family, who have been most patient and
encouraging;

And to my many friends who urged me to produce
the book.

Your compilation of Arabic quotations is a fascinating collection. The quotations, together with the illuminating commentary, reveal the richness and wisdom of the culture that produced them. And you may quote me!

Henry A. Kissinger

As a person who has known the author for years and who, like him, has bridged the bi-cultural gap, I rejoice at the publication of *"As The Arabs Say..."* The contents are not only fascinating, but also timely in that they give the English-speaking reader an insight into Islamic values and Arab thought—a necessary prerequisite to fruitful communication with the peoples of the vast Arab and Muslim areas. All those who have known Isa Khalil Sabbagh would testify that there is more, much more, where this came from.

This book is like a rare gem; it did not have to be voluminous to be precious.

Fouad Al-Farsy, Ph.D.
Deputy Minister of Industry & Electricity
Riyadh, Kingdom of Saudi Arabia

as we move in the right-hand direction along the scale. For instance, the distance lying between graduations 1 and 2 is about 12 mm. In this same space between graduations 16 and 32, it would be necessary to crowd in 16 smaller spaces.

The scales of Fig. 2 are logarithmic, and you will understand their properties when you have perused the section on logarithms. (There is no necessity to break off at this stage to read about logarithms, and we recommend that you read on without concern for them.) Fig. 1 gave us the sum of 4 and 2. Fig. 2 gives us the product of 4 and 2, i.e. 8, and it becomes evident that one of the rules of logarithms is that by adding them together we are effecting multiplication of numbers, and when we subtract one from another we are dividing.

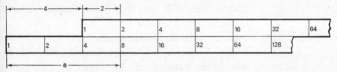

Fig. 2

In these simple facts lies the principle of our slide rule, which, in effect, is the equivalent of a table of logarithms arranged in a convenient form for rapid working.

Further study of Fig. 2 will show that the scales are set so that we can at once read off $4 \times 2 = 8$; $4 \times 4 = 16$; $4 \times 8 = 32$; and if the scale had been extended and subdivided we should have been able to read off many other results.

The procedure for multiplication of two factors is:

(a) Select any one of the factors and note its position in the lower scale.

(b) Slide the upper scale to the right, to bring the 1 of this scale opposite the factor noted in the lower scale.

(c) Find the second factor in the upper scale.

(d) Directly below the second factor, read the number which you will see in the lower scale. This number is the answer to the multiplication of these two factors.

We know that these instructions, when written, sound rather forbidding, but they are quite simple in execution and if the reader will follow them through carefully he will, in the course of a few minutes, learn to use the two scales for multiplication. It will certainly assist if the scales are drawn out on two strips of cardboard, so that they can be moved along one another into the different positions.

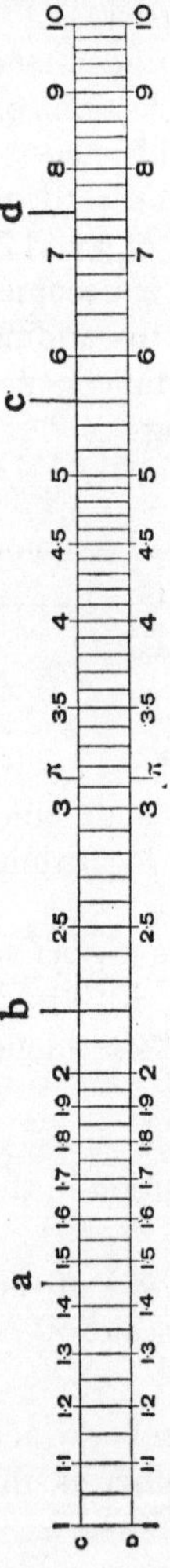

Division is effected by using the scales to subtract the logarithm of the divisor from the logarithm of the dividend. Referring once more to Fig. 2, we see at once that in order to divide, say, 128 by 32 we slide the upper scale along until the 32 in it stands immediately above the 128 in the lower scale. Then opposite the 1 of the upper scale we read the answer, 4, in the lower scale.

Fig. 3 shows you a logarithmic scale which has been subdivided between the primary numbers. You will notice that between graduations 1 and 2 it has been possible to show twenty smaller spaces, whereas between 9 and 10 only 5 subdivisions have been made. This change in the distance between consecutive lines is a feature of all logarithmic scales; it is the crowding together we have mentioned earlier.

We now come to what may prove a difficulty for some readers to whom scales are not familiar. We refer to what is generally termed "reading the scales". We will, therefore, spend a little time in studying this difficulty since it is quite certain that ability to read the scales easily and with certainty is essential. The difficulty—if there is any—lies in the fact that the graduations of the scale alter. In Fig. 3, the distance between 1 and 2 is subdivided into

FIG. 3

20 parts. If the subdivision continued in the same way, the spaces would soon become inconveniently small. At the division 2 a change in the dividing occurs, and the space between 2 and 3 is subdivided into only 10 parts, and this subdividing continues from 3 to 4 and again from 4 to 5. At 5 another change becomes necessary and the main divisions from 5 to 10 are now subdivided, each into five parts only.

In reading any position of the scale, the graduations on either side of that position must be examined. Look along the scale to the nearest main figure, then note whether the subdivisions are tenths or fifths or any other fractions of the main division. With a very little practice you will quickly develop the faculty of reading the positions in the scale with a high degree of accuracy.

As examples let us attempt to read the positions in the scale of the four lines marked a, b, c and d of Fig. 3. Line a exactly coincides with a division of the scale and appears to be about midway between 1·4 and 1·5. The position of the line a, therefore, is 1·45. Line b also coincides with a division of the scale and lies between main numbers 2 and 3. A glance shows that there are ten subdivisions between 2 and 3. The graduation immediately to the right of 2 is 2·1, and the next to the right is 2·2, and it is at this position that line b stands. Line c lies between numbers 5 and 6, and now we find there are only 5 subdivisions in this space. We will write down fully the readings of the lines at this part of the scale; they are 5·0, 5·2, 5·4, 5·6, 5·8 and 6·0. Line c clearly stands at 5·6. Line d does not coincide with any graduation in the scale and now our ability to estimate fractions must be exercised. Line d lies between 7·4 and 7·6. Let us try to visualise the small distance between these two lines being further subdivided into five smaller spaces. There would now be four lines very close to one another in between the lines at 7·4 and 7·6, and the readings of these four lines would be 7·44, 7·48, 7·52, 7·56, and we estimate that line d is very near to 7·48.

The observant reader may object with some justification that there is a fundamental error involved in the method we have adopted in arriving at the value 7·48. He will have noticed that in effect we have estimated the position of the line *d* as being 2/5ths of the distance between 7·4 and 7·6, and he will point out that even if our estimate is quite correct the true position of the imaginary line 7·48 is not exactly at this point because, the scale being logarithmic, the five small spaces between 7·4 and 7·6 are not equal to one another. Actually the imaginary 7·48 line is slightly to the right of the position we have assigned to it. This is typical of the errors we invariably make when we estimate the positions of points which do not coincide with any real lines in the scale. We shall return to this matter when we consider later on the degree of accuracy possible when using a slide rule, but the inquisitive reader may care to know that the true scale reading of a point *exactly* 2/5ths of the distance along 7·4–7·6 of the scale is 7·476. Our estimate has involved us in the small error of 4 parts in 7000. To obtain an idea of what this error means, imagine you are asked to measure the length of the table at which you are working. By means of a rule or tape and measuring carefully you find the length is, say, 1400 mm, whereas when measured with more precise apparatus the length is found to be 1402·5 mm; the error you have made is, therefore, 2·5 mm, and proportionately these two errors are nearly equal.

Fig. 4 illustrates two scales set so that we can multiply 3 by various numbers. Notice that, directly under any number in the upper scale, three times that number appears in the lower scale, e.g. $3 \times 11 = 33$, $3 \times 12 = 36$, $3 \times 2 = 6$ and several others. This same setting of the scales shows how we can divide 9 by 3, or 6 by 2, etc. Now, in Fig. 4 the upper scale projects to the right beyond the lower, and we cannot read results directly under the projecting part. This difficulty is surmounted by sliding the upper scale to the left a distance equal to its own length ("traversing the slide"), and Fig. 5 shows these new positions of the scales and now we can perform multiplications such as $4 \times 3 = 12$, $6 \times 3 = 18$, $9 \times 3 = 27$, and we can also divide 18 by 6 or 15 by 5, etc.

We do not wish to weary the reader by pursuing unduly

Fig. 4

Fig. 5

this very elementary conception of the slide rule. This book is primarily designed to assist readers who have had no previous acquaintance with the slide rule, and we think that those who have persevered so far will, by now, realise that there is nothing difficult to learn and that the manipulation of a slide rule is very simple indeed.

We feel that we should now pass on to examine the slide rule in its modern practical form.

(The next section deals with fractions and decimals. It is included to assist readers who may have difficulty in reading the scales in the decimal system. It should be ignored by others.)

SECTION TWO

FRACTIONS—DECIMALS

THE logarithmic scales of slide rules are, with a few exceptions, subdivided into decimal fractions, or, as we more often say, into decimals. It is impossible to take practical advantage of the slide rule without a working knowledge of the decimal system. We believe a brief note of explanation may assist those readers who think that the slide rule is useless to them because they cannot easily work in decimals. This section is not intended for readers who are familiar with the decimal system and can use it without difficulty.

We propose to start with a short reference to ordinary fractions. The word fraction means "a part". Thus when we speak of $\frac{1}{2}$ a millimetre—which is sometimes called an ordinary fraction, as distinct from a decimal fraction—we think of a length of one millimetre being divided into two equal parts, of which we take one part. When we mention $\frac{3}{4}$ as a fraction, we think of something, say a metre, or an hour, or a penny, being divided into four equal parts, of which we take three. The upper figure of an ordinary fraction is called the numerator, and the lower figure the denominator. A fraction in which the numerator is smaller than the denominator is always less than 1, and is sometimes called a proper fraction. A fraction such as $\frac{7}{5}$, in which the numerator is larger than the denominator, is called an "improper" fraction. These terms proper and improper, when referred to fractions, are of no practical importance.

The value of a fraction is not altered if we multiply or divide numerator and denominator by any number. For instance,

$$\frac{3}{5} = \frac{3 \times 4}{5 \times 4} = \frac{12}{20} = \frac{12 \times 2}{20 \times 2} = \frac{24}{40}.$$

The fractions $\frac{3}{5}$, $\frac{12}{20}$ and $\frac{24}{40}$ are all exactly equal to one another, but we may say that the $\frac{3}{5}$ is the simplest form, and in general this is the way it is written. You will see that the fraction $\frac{24}{40}$ can be reduced to $\frac{3}{5}$ by dividing both numerator and denominator by 8. This kind of simplification is called cancelling.

Addition and Subtraction

To add together two or more fractions we express them in terms of a common denominator, and then add together the numerators.

Example: Add together $\frac{2}{3}$ and $\frac{4}{5}$.

$$\frac{2}{3} + \frac{4}{5} = \frac{(2 \times 5)}{(3 \times 5)} + \frac{(4 \times 3)}{(5 \times 3)} = \frac{10}{15} + \frac{12}{15} = \frac{22}{15}.$$

Result is $\frac{22}{15}$ or $1\frac{7}{15}$.

Problem 1. Add together $\frac{1}{6} + \frac{1}{4} + \frac{2}{5}$.

Subtraction of one fraction from another is effected in a similar manner.

Example: Find the result of taking $\frac{1}{6}$ from $\frac{3}{8}$.

The smallest number which is a multiple of 6 and 8 is 24.

$$\frac{3}{8} - \frac{1}{6} = \frac{(3 \times 3)}{(8 \times 3)} - \frac{(1 \times 4)}{(6 \times 4)} = \frac{9}{24} - \frac{4}{24} = \frac{5}{24}.$$

Multiplication and Division

To multiply together two or more fractions it is only necessary to multiply together all the numerators to form the numerator of the result and to multiply all the denominators to obtain the denominator of the result.

Example: Evaluate $\dfrac{2}{3} \times \dfrac{4}{5} \times \dfrac{2}{7} = \dfrac{2 \times 4 \times 2}{3 \times 5 \times 7} = \dfrac{16}{105}.$

Cancellation of numbers common to both numerator and denominator should be effected whenever possible since this leads to simplification.

Example: Evaluate $\frac{1}{3} \times \frac{3}{5} \times 1\frac{1}{4}$.

This may be written $\frac{1}{3} \times \frac{3}{5} \times \frac{5}{4} = \frac{1}{4}$, the 3's and 5's cancelling out leaving only the 1 in the numerator and the 4 in the denominator.

Problem 2. Evaluate $1\frac{3}{5} \times \frac{3}{4} \times 2\frac{1}{6}$.

Division may be regarded as a special case of multiplication. To divide a number by a fraction you may interchange the numerator and denominator of the divisor, and then multiply by the inverted factor. An easy example is that of dividing by 2, which is exactly the same as multiplying by a $\frac{1}{2}$.

Example: Divide $\frac{3}{4}$ by $\frac{2}{5}$.

This should be written $\frac{3}{4} \times \frac{5}{2} = \frac{15}{8} = 1\frac{7}{8}$.

Problem 3. Divide the product of $\frac{3}{8}$ and $2\frac{1}{5}$ by $\frac{3}{4}$.

Decimals

The word decimal is derived from the Latin word meaning ten, and the decimal system is based on 10. Consider, for example, the number 8888: it is built up of $8000 + 800 + 80 + 8$. It is evident that the 8's are not all of equal value and importance. The first 8 expresses the number of thousands, the second the number of hundreds, the third the number of tens and the last the number of units.

We have used the number consisting of the same figure 8 four times; this was done because we wished to emphasise that the same figure can have different values attached to it, depending upon its position in the group. The number might have included any or all of the figures from 0 to 9 arranged in an infinite number of ways.

Let us consider a simpler number, say 15. In this the 1 actually means 10 units, and the 5 represents 5 units. Now we might desire to add a fraction to the 15 making it, say, $15\frac{1}{2}$, and it seems feasible to do so by extending beyond the units figure this system of numbering by 10's. To indicate the end of a whole number we write a dot, called the decimal point, and any figures on the right-hand side of it represent a part or fraction of a unit.

We have seen that any figure in the fourth place to the left, counting from the units figure, represents so many thousands, the next to the right so many hundreds, and next so many tens, and the next so many units. If we continue we shall here pass the decimal point, and the next figure to the right must represent so many tenths of a unit. Still moving to the right the next figure will represent so many hundredths, the next so many thousandths, and so on indefinitely.

Now, $\frac{1}{2}$ is $\frac{5}{10}$ and, remembering that the figure immediately to the right of the decimal point represents so many tenths, we can express $15\frac{1}{2}$ by 15·5. Instead of saying fifteen and a half, we should say fifteen decimal five or, as is more usual, fifteen point five. It would not be incorrect to express 15·5 by 15·50, or by 15·5000; the final noughts in both these cases are unnecessary but not actually wrong. In the form of a common fraction, the ·50 means $\frac{50}{100}$ which cancels to $\frac{5}{10}$, and finally to $\frac{1}{2}$, and similarly ·5000 as a common fraction becomes $\frac{5000}{10000}$ which also cancels to $\frac{1}{2}$.

We sometimes see one or more noughts preceding a whole number, e.g. 018. The nought has no significance, and is only used when for some reason we wish to have the same number of figures in a series of numbers. 018 means 18, and 002 means 2. We must understand that one or more noughts at the beginning of a whole number, and noughts following the decimal part of a number, do not alter the value of the number.

Conversion of Decimal Fractions into Ordinary Fractions

It is easy to convert a decimal fraction into an ordinary fraction. Take as an example the number 46·823, which means

46 units and a fraction of a unit. Earlier we have said that the first figure to the right of the decimal point indicates so many tenths of a unit, the next to the right so many hundredths, and the next so many thousandths of a unit. We have, therefore,

$46 + \frac{8}{10} + \frac{2}{100} + \frac{3}{1000}$ which may be written $46 + \frac{800}{1000} + \frac{20}{1000} + \frac{3}{1000}$ which reduces to $46\frac{823}{1000}$.

From this we deduce the simple rule for converting a decimal fraction into an ordinary fraction. As the numerator of the fraction, write all the figures following the decimal point, and for the denominator write a 1, followed by as many noughts as there are figures in the numerator.

Example: $152 \cdot 61 = 152\frac{61}{100}$. $\qquad 9 \cdot 903 = 9\frac{903}{1000}$.

Problem 4. Convert the following into numbers and common fractions expressed in the simplest forms: 6·8, 13·08, 19·080, 20·125, 41·0125, 86·625.

There is a different rule for recurring decimals which will be given later.

Addition and Subtraction

When numbers include fractions it is easy to effect addition or subtraction in the decimal notation. It is only necessary to write down the numbers so that their decimal points are in a vertical line, then add or subtract in the usual manner, and insert the decimal point in the answer immediately below the decimal points of the original figures.

Example: Add together 16·26, 8·041 and 186·902.

$$
\begin{array}{r}
16 \cdot 26 \\
8 \cdot 041 \\
186 \cdot 902 \\
\hline
211 \cdot 203 \\
\end{array}
$$

Subtract 108·694 from 423·47.

$$423·470$$
$$108·694$$

$$\overline{314·776}$$

Problem 5. Add together 12·801, ·92, 5·002 and 11·0.
Subtract 82·607 from 96·2.

Multiplication and Division

A number expressed in the decimal system is very easily multiplied by or divided by 10 or 100, etc. To multiply by 10, move the decimal point one place to the right; to multiply by 100, move the decimal point two places to the right, and so on. When dividing move the decimal point to the left one place for each division by 10.

Examples:
$$61·24 \times 10 = 612·4$$
$$61·24 \times 100 = 6124$$
$$61·24 \times 1000 = 61240$$
$$61·24 \div 10 = 6·124$$
$$61·24 \div 100 = ·6124$$
$$61·24 \div 1000 = ·06124$$

Multiplication, when neither of the factors is 10 (or an integral power of 10, i.e. 100, 1000, etc.), should be carried out in the usual way, and the position of the decimal point ignored until the product is obtained. The number of decimal figures in the answer is easily obtained; it is equal to the sum of the numbers of figures after the decimal points of the factors.

Example: Multiply 62·743 by 8·6.

$$62·743$$
$$8·6$$
$$\overline{501·944}$$
$$37·6458$$
$$\overline{539·5898}$$

Here there are $3+1=4$ decimal figures in the two factors. Starting from the last figure in the product we count off 4 decimal figures and insert the decimal point.

Problem 6. Multiply 9·274 by 82·6.

When dividing in the decimal notation it is advisable to convert the divisor into a whole number by moving the decimal point. If the decimal point of the dividend is moved the same number of places and in the same direction, the result will not be affected by these changes.

The following example will make this procedure clear.

Example: Divide 896·41 by 22·5.

```
                              39·8
Here the result is 39·8. The   225)8964·1
next figure in the answer      675
would be a 4, so that if the   ────
result is required to only one 2214
decimal place it is 39·8.      2025
                               ────
                               1891
                               1800
                               ────
                                910
```

Had the next figure been 5 or over 5, the result would then be given as 39·9, since this result would have been nearer to the exact answer than 39·8. When a numerical result which does not divide out exactly is to be expressed to a stated number of places of decimals, the division should be carried to one further decimal place. If this additional figure is less than 5 the figure preceding it should be left unaltered, but if the additional figure is 5 or over the preceding figure should be increased by 1.

Contracted Methods

When the factors which enter into the operations of multiplication or division are large, contracted methods should be used. This section is not intended to deal with all arithmetical rules and processes, but the reader will find a chapter dealing with contracted methods in books on elementary mathematics.

Conversion of Ordinary Fractions into Decimal Fractions

An ordinary fraction can be converted into a decimal expression by dividing the numerator by denominator. If we desire to change $\frac{3}{4}$ into decimals, we divide 3·00 by 4. We generally add noughts to the 3 as shown. This is a case of simple division which we should often work mentally, but for the sake of clarity we will write it out in full.

Now 4 will not divide into 3, so we include
4)3·00   with the 3 the 0 which follows it and divide
·75   4 into 30. This gives 7 with 2 over and the 2
with the next 0 makes 20, which divides by 4 and gives 5 with no remainder. We insert the decimal point immediately below the decimal point in the original number and so obtain ·75 as the decimal equivalent of $\frac{3}{4}$.

Examples: Express as decimals $\frac{5}{8}$ and $\frac{17}{25}$.

$$
\begin{array}{r}
·68 \\
25)17·00 \\
150 \\
\hline
\end{array}
$$

$$
\begin{array}{r}
8)5·000 \\
\hline
·625 \\
\end{array}
$$

$$
\begin{array}{r}
200 \\
200 \\
\end{array}
$$

Problem 7. Express as decimals $\frac{7}{8}$ and $\frac{13}{16}$.

The reader will see that we can convert an ordinary fraction into a decimal fraction by converting the fraction into a form in which the denominator is 10 or 100 or 1000, as the mathematicians say, into a positive integral power of 10.

Reverting to the $\frac{17}{25}$ considered a little earlier, we can convert the 25 into 100 by multiplying by 4, but to maintain the value of the fraction unaltered we must also multiply the 17 by 4.

We have, therefore,

$$\frac{17}{25} = \frac{17 \times 4}{25 \times 4} = \frac{68}{100} = \cdot68.$$

This method of conversion is sometimes quicker and easier than dividing denominator into numerator.

Recurring Decimals

If we attempt to convert the fraction $\frac{1}{3}$ into decimals by division, we obtain a result which is unending.

$$\frac{3)1\cdot0000}{\cdot3333\ldots}$$

This result is said to be a recurring decimal and is often written $\cdot\dot{3}$. The dot over the 3 indicates that the $\dot{3}$ is repeated indefinitely.

A number such as $24\cdot82\dot{1}\dot{6}$, means $24\cdot82161616$—the 16 being repeated indefinitely.

Conversion of Recurring Decimals into Ordinary Fractions

The rule to which we refer earlier is:

Subtract the figures which do not repeat from the whole of the decimal expression and divide by a number made up of a 9 for each recurring figure, and a 0 for each non-recurring figure.

Example: Convert $14\cdot6\dot{4}\dot{2}$ into an ordinary fraction.

$$\begin{array}{r} 642 \\ 6 \\ \hline 636 \end{array}$$ Result $14\frac{636}{990} = 14\frac{106}{165}.$

Problem 8. Convert $2\cdot83\dot{1}\dot{3}$ into an ordinary fraction. Check the result by dividing denominator into numerator to see if $2\cdot83\dot{1}\dot{3}$ results.

THE MODERN SLIDE RULE

THE simple slide rule, consisting of two logarithmic scales drawn on strips of cardboard, mentioned in Section 1 would, in actual practice, be inconvenient to use. Clearly the two scales should be linked together by some means so that, whilst they could be made to slide to and fro along one another, they would, when set, retain their positions and not fall apart. In order to mark any point in a scale when desired, a movable index would be a useful adjunct to the scales. We shall find that these points have not been overlooked in the slide rule as we find it to-day.

We do not propose to write a long description of the modern slide rule. We assume that the reader possesses a slide rule, or, at least, has access to one, and the mechanical construction of the instrument is so straightforward that we would not presume to enter into superfluous details.

There are a few points which we believe may be mentioned with advantage, and we think illustrations of a de-luxe instrument, and also an inexpensive type, should be included in this section. These are shown in Figs. 6 and 7 respectively.

Protection of Slide Rule

Whatever type of slide rule you decide to buy we ask you to take great care of it. The manufacture of slide rules is a technical and highly skilled craft, and much painstaking effort goes into their production. Your slide rule should be protected from exposure to heat and damp. You should particularly avoid leaving it lying exposed to the direct rays of the sun in warm weather. The majority of slide rules are constructed in plastic; this material discolours and shrinks if unduly exposed

When not in use please replace the rule in the protective case supplied with it, and put away in a cool, dry place, preferably in the drawer of your desk.

Component Parts

Since we frequently refer to them, we think we should mention the names of the component parts of a slide rule. The body of the rule is usually termed the "stock". The smaller part, which can be moved to right or left, is called the "slide", and the movable index is known as the "cursor", or indicator.

If you will examine the stock you will find it is built up of several parts which give it a degree of flexibility. If the stock was just a solid strip of wood with the necessary grooves machined in it to accommodate the slide and the cursor, it would inevitably, in the course of time, warp sufficiently to grip the slide tightly and make the manipulation of the rule difficult or impossible. We have seen such rules with the slides so tight that it has been necessary to use a hammer or something similar to drive the slides out.

Sizes of Slide Rules

The 250 mm rule is the popular size. In this the scales are 25 cm in length, and the overall length of the rule 28-30 cm. More convenient to carry in the pocket is the $12\frac{1}{2}$ cm rule. There are also available rules of lengths 40 or 50 cm or more. The Unique Slide Rule Company markets a range of 18 cm models, an intermediate length which permits the same degree of subdividing as in 25 cm models.

Cylindrical and circular instruments are made which employ the logarithmic principles and these are commonly called slide rules, although the term is certainly not appropriate. We shall make a brief mention of these instruments at a later stage.

C and D Scales

You will notice that there are several scales on the rule. The layout of scales is varied to adapt the rule to different require-

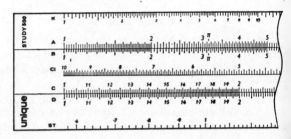

Fig. 6

ments. If your rule is one of the general-purpose type it will be equipped, among others, with two scales, usually denoted by the letters C and D. Scale C lies along the bottom edge of the slide, and scale D is on the stock adjacent to scale C. These two scales are identical in their graduations and are, in reality, one single scale which has been cut through lengthwise. The main graduations of scales C and D are numbered 1, 2, 3, etc. up to 10. Subdivisions should be numbered as fully as possible without carrying the process to the extent of causing confusion. The scales of some slide rules are numbered in a very confusing manner. We contend that when subdivisions are numbered the figure marked on them should be exact and not abbreviated. In some of the higher-priced rules the principal subdivisions between main divisions 1 and 2 of scales C and D are marked 1, 2, 3, etc., up to 9. These figures should be 1·1, 1·2, 1·3, etc. up to 1·9. This omission may strike the reader as curious. The reason for it is believed to be as follows: many decades ago when slide rules were virtually hand-produced, the figuring was done by hand stamping and the range 1·1 to 1·9 was abbreviated in this way to save time. Even comparatively recently some outlets of the U.S.A. have demanded rules calibrated in this misleading manner because it fitted their teaching techniques and written texts on slide rule use. We recommend the reader to avoid purchasing a rule in which the

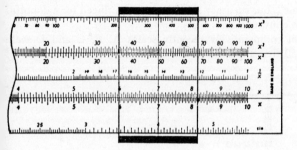

scale numbering is abbreviated, as it will inevitably involve him in errors due to misreading the scales.

Scales C and D are those most frequently used of all; we have mentioned them first and shall return to them in Section 4.

A and B Scales

Scales A and B lie adjacent to one another, A on the stock and B along the upper edge of the slide.

The numbering of the main divisions of scales A and B, starting from the left-hand end, should be 1, 2, 3, etc., up to 10, then 20, 30, etc., up to 100. The figure 10 marks the line mid-way along the length of the scale. The principal subdivisions should also be numbered as far as conveniently possible. Abbreviated figures should be avoided for the reason mentioned earlier.

At this stage we would ask you in all seriousness not to acquire the very bad habit of using Scales A and B for multiplication and division. The objection to this practice lies in

the fact that when the A and B scales of a 25 cm rule are so
used the instrument, in effect, becomes a 12½ cm rule, and
results cannot be obtained with the same degree of accuracy
as when the C and D scales are used. It is true that when
scales A and B are employed the results need never be "off
the scale", but accuracy should not be sacrificed for a doubtful
gain in convenience.

Until comparatively recently scales A, B, C and D were
often all that appeared on the face of the rule. As a result of

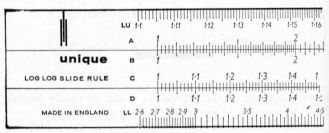

Fig. 7

the change in manufacturing technique referred to earlier, it
became possible to include other scales without increasing
production costs to any great extent. "Unique" slide rules,
almost since their inception, have carried log-log scales in
many models, and these scales are now taken for granted.
Their inclusion certainly adds value to a slide rule. They are
not difficult to understand, as will be shown presently.

In the absence of log-log scales the combination of the A,
B, C and D scales is probably the best that could be devised
but if a slide rule is equipped with log-log scales we think the
provision of the A and B scales is unnecessary, and that other
scales can be substituted for them which increase the useful-
ness of the rule. Sections 9, 10 and 12 deal with rules designed
on these lines.

Scales A and B in conjunction with scales C and D give a

quick means of extracting square and cube roots, and of squaring and cubing numbers. Since scale D is twice the length of each of the identical halves of scale A, it follows that in moving along scale A you will be passing the logarithmic "milestones" twice as fast as when moving along scale D. Now, if you double the logarithm of a number, you will arrive at the logarithm of the square of that number. Please examine your rule and with the aid of a cursor project readings in scale D to scale A—or from scale C to scale B—on the slide. You will

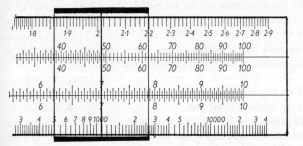

see that opposite 2 in D appears 4 in A, and for every number in D the square of that number appears in A.

Square roots are very quickly obtained by reversing the process and projecting from scale A into scale D. The problems of cubing numbers and extracting cube roots are in like manner facilitated by using the four scales A, B, C and D, and we shall return to this problem at a later stage.

If log-log scales are included in your slide rule, *all* powers and roots of numbers may be evaluated easily, and it is for this reason we say that the A and B scales are of doubtful value, since their uses in the processes of evolution and involution are very limited. Log-log scales give the means, in conjunction with scale D, of evaluating any power or any root of any number, whereas scales A and B will only deal with powers and roots of 2 or 3, and multiples of 2 or 3.

Log-log Scales

We have mentioned log-log scales several times. When included in a slide rule these scales are often placed along the top and bottom edges of the stock. Please refer to Fig. 7 and you will see the log-log scales; they are marked LU and LL, at the left-hand end of the rule. Log-log scales are very useful in dealing with certain technical problems. We have heard the opinion expressed that log-log scales give the appearance of complexity to the face of the slide rule and, since they are seldom used, should not be included. We do not agree. The log-log scales are not obtrusive, and one quickly learns to ignore them when not required, and we have not found them inconvenient or confusing. They are sometimes to be found on the reverse of the slide, as mentioned later on.

Section 6 deals with the problems which demand the provision of log-log scales and which cannot be solved by the slide rule without their aid.

The primary object of this book is to attempt to remove the impression that the slide rule is a difficult instrument to use. If, therefore, any reader feels that he prefers the very simplest slide rule with only the A, B, C and D scales included, we agree that he may be well advised to use this type, especially if his work is of a straightforward nature and not likely to involve the use of log-log or trigonometrical scales.

Sine and Tangent Scales

If you will look at the undersurface of the slide of your rule you will probably see two or perhaps three scales.

The scale marked S is a scale of sines. Its graduation will probably commence at a value of 35 minutes—marked 35'—and finish at 90°. This scale is used in conjunction with scale A.

The tangent scale will be labelled T. Graduations may start just below 6° and proceed to 45°. Alternatively, the tan scale may start at 34' and finish at 45°. In the former case the T scale is used in conjunction with the D scale; in the latter case it is used with the A scale.

In some rules the S and T scales appear on the face of the rule. Some people prefer this arrangement of scales, and the manufacture of the rule is simplified when it is adopted. The disadvantage lies in the fact that the face of the rule becomes somewhat congested with these additional scales.

If you will look carefully at the S and T scales you may see that, unlike the A, B, C and D, and log-log scales, they are not subdivided consistently in tenths, fifths, etc. Below 20° on the S scale, and throughout the T scale, the unit divisions are subdivided into sixths, twelfths, etc. This system of subdivision is adopted because we do not always work in decimals of a degree, but we use the corresponding number of minutes, and as you will see subdivision into sixths, etc., is more convenient for this purpose, there being 60 minutes in one degree.

In recent years manufacturers have adopted the practice of subdividing in decimals to the S and T scales. The reader may encounter slide rules in which the minutes' graduations have given place to decimals of degrees.

Section 7 deals with examples of trigonometrical work employing scales S or T.

Log Scale

The third scale on the reverse side of the slide is often an evenly divided scale, usually marked L, which enables us in conjunction with scale D to read off logarithms of numbers. If the scales on your rule are 25 cm long, you will see that the log scale is subdivided into tenths and fiftieths, and it is, in effect, a 25 cm measuring rule. As a matter of fact, you can obtain logarithms of numbers with the aid of an ordinary rule used in conjunction with scale C or D.

The scales mentioned in this section are, with the exception of the log-log scales, those you will find in the ordinary or standard type of slide rule—the type which seems to be preferred by the large majority of users. In later sections we shall deal with slide rules provided with different arrangements of scales.

The Cursor

In closing this section we would add a note of warning concerning the cursor. We strongly recommend the reader to purchase a slide rule which is fitted with a "free-view" cursor. The best type of cursor is that which has supports on only its top and bottom edges for engaging with the grooves in the stock. Some types have a light rectangle frame into which the glass or celluloid window is fitted. The edges of the frame lie across the face of the rule and obliterate to some extent the figures and graduations of the scales, and create an element of uncertainty and add to the possibility of making errors. One form of cursor, now only occasionally seen, has fitted on one side of it a small index and scale, designed to assist in fixing the position of the decimal point in the numerical result. This form of cursor hides a considerable part of the scales and generally is a source of annoyance.

On some cursors you may find two or three hair lines. The additional lines give assistance in calculations concerning areas of circles, etc. Confusion may arise when multiple-line cursors are used, and we prefer the simple free-view cursor with a single hair line.

Linear Scales

We would say a word concerning the linear scales which are often fitted to slide rules. These have no connection with the rule as a calculating device. They add to the appearance of a rule, but we think they are entirely superfluous. A slide rule should be always handled carefully, and it is one of the minor annoyances in life to see it used for ruling lines or to take measurements when a wooden or plastic office ruler, or a steel rule, should be used.

C AND D SCALES

IN this section appear the first examples involving the aid of a slide rule. In the condensed instructions, we shall adopt abbreviations, namely: C for scale C; D for scale D; 12C means line 12 in scale C; X refers to the index line of the cursor.

Examples are worked to assist the student. **Problems** are inserted for the student to solve. Answers to problems are given at the end of the book.

This section is devoted to those operations most often effected by slide rules; those which every student must first learn: multiplication and division.

We have in Section 3 advised the reader to refrain from using scales A and B for multiplication and division, and we shall confine our attention to scales C and D. Throughout this section no mention will be made of the other scales, which, for the time being, you should ignore.

Scales C and D are subdivided in decimals, and we must now assume that you are able to read them without difficulty. Fig. 8 illustrates the C and D scales as you should find them in practically all 25 cm rules. In order to illustrate them full size, we show in the upper part the left-hand half and in the lower part the right-hand half of the scales. To show the scales complete in one length would necessitate them being reduced in size in order to print them on a page of this book; this would make some of the divisions inconveniently small and difficult to read.

Problem 9. You are asked to read the positions of the lines marked in Fig. 8 and compare your reading with those we give in the answers to problems. If you feel confident that

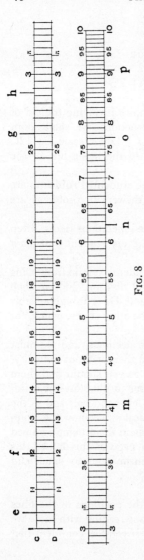

FIG. 8

you are able to read the scales we
can safely proceed. If you have any
difficulty we ask you to turn back
to Section 1 and study that part
dealing with reading scales or, better,
to enlist the aid of someone conver-
sant with scales. A few minutes of
oral explanation will assist more
than pages of written notes which
would be too tedious to be endured.

Multiplication

Let us examine these four simple
examples:

$$12 \times 32 = 384$$
$$1 \cdot 2 \times 3 \cdot 2 = 3 \cdot 84$$
$$\cdot 012 \times \cdot 032 = \cdot 000384$$
$$120 \times 320 = 38400$$

In every case, if we ignore the
position of the decimal point and
the noughts which precede or follow
the significant figures, we are concerned only with the multiplication
of 12×32. You will notice that the
answer in each case has only the
three significant figures, 384. If we
use a slide rule to carry out these
four multiplications the operation
would be identical.

The line marked f in Fig. 8 is
drawn to coincide with the 1-
graduation. In some rules this line
may be marked 2, and if such is the
case you will be using a rule with
the abbreviated marking to which we

have referred earlier. Try to secure a rule in which the C and D scales are numbered as in Fig. 8.

1·2 graduation may, for our purpose, be read as 1·2, or 12, or ·012, or 120, or any combination of figures in which 12 stand together followed or preceded by any number of noughts. If, however, we read this line as 102 we shall be making a fundamental error, and our result would be incorrect. You will, no doubt, have found the line 1·02 in connection with Problem 9. It is the line marked *e*.

We will now see how the result 384 is derived from the two factors 12 and 32. You will understand that we are dealing with simple numbers for the purpose of instruction. Obviously there is no other point in using a slide rule to compute results which could easily be obtained without its aid.

If at any time you are in doubt as to whether you are using your slide rule correctly, always work out an elementary example with simple figures so that you can check the slide rule result. We tender this advice more particularly when complicated examples may arise, or when the reader is using scales which he seldom needs.

Example: Multiply 12 by 32.

> Find 12 in scale D; move the slide to the right to bring the 1 of scale C coincident with the 12 of scale D. Directly under the 32 in scale C you will find the result, 384, in scale D.

We have described the two operations fully, but we repeat them below in the condensed form we shall hereafter use. If you will get familiar with the condensed form, you will find it much less tedious to follow than a wordy description, and typography is reduced. The description started by saying: find the 12 in scale D. You may just note the 12 in scale D by eye, or, if you prefer it, place the cursor index over it. If the cursor is used, an additional mechanical operation is involved, but we think it is the easier method to adopt; this is a matter of opinion, and you may please yourself. We shall make no reference to using the cursor for picking up the first or final readings.

In the condensed form the operations would be:

To 12D set 1C. Under 32C read result, 384, in D.

If we had been multiplying 32 by 10 the answer would have been 320. Our answer must be rather greater than 320 since we are really multiplying by 12, and we therefore write it as 384. The answer could not be 38·4, nor could it be 3840. We hope you will understand that, having obtained the figures 384 from our slide rule, we must determine the "order" of the result, or, in other words, find the position of the decimal point.

> **Example:** Find the area in square metres of a rectangular plate measuring 4·8 m × 6·4 m.
>
> To 48D set 10C. Under 64C read 307 in D.
>
> Position of the decimal point is determined by inspection of the two factors. We obtain an approximate answer by taking the factors as 5 and 6; in doing this you will notice that we have increased 4·8 to 5 and reduced 6·4 to 6. The product of 5 times 6 = 30 must be fairly near the true result, and we may, therefore, insert the decimal point, making our answer 30·7 m².

There are other methods of determining the position of the decimal point, but we think at this stage you would find them very difficult to understand. We mention them at the end of this section, but we advise you always to adopt the approximation method of finding the position of the decimal point.

In the example 4·8 × 6·4 you will notice that, if we set the 1 of C to 48 of D, then the 64 of C is "off the scale" of D, and we must move the slide to bring the 10 of C to coincide with the 48 of D to obtain a reading. The necessity of re-setting the slide does sometimes occur when we are using scales C and D, but when we have a little experience of using a slide rule we seem to acquire an instinct which warns us when we are using the wrong end of scale C. When setting the 1 or 10 of C, you should move the slide roughly into position and then take a quick glance at the factor in C which you wish to use. If this factor lies over some part of scale D you can proceed accurately to adjust the slide and obtain your result. Occasionally the factor in C is only slightly outside the scale of D. Sometimes there are a few graduation lines on the left-hand side of the 1 of scale C and D, and also a few graduations on the right-hand of the 10 of these scales. These extensions of the scales are sometimes useful for picking up a result which otherwise would be just off the scale. The graduations to the right of the 10 are identical with those immediately to the right of the 1, and those which lie to the left of the 1 are the same as those which precede the 10. These extensions are short additions of the C and D scales.

Example: Calculate the cost of a certain substance 40·5 mm long × 28·7 mm wide × ·625 mm thick at 26p per mm³.

We have four factors to evaluate, $40·5 \times 28·7 \times ·625 \times ·26$.

To 405D set 10C. X to 287, 1C to X. X to 625C. 10C to X.

Result 189D under 26C.

Approximation: ·26 is slightly more than a $\frac{1}{4}$, and $\frac{1}{4}$ of 40 is 10. ·625 $(= \frac{5}{8})$ of 28 is somewhere near 18. 10 times $18 = 180$ and the answer must be 189p or £1·89. (The positions of the four necessary readings are marked in Fig. 8 to assist those who may still have difficulty in reading the scale.)

You are now requested to repeat the foregoing example by taking the factors in different orders. Start, say, with the ·625 and multiply by 40·5, then by ·26, and finally by 28·7. The result should be the same, irrespective of the order in which the factors are selected. With four factors there are possible 24 different sequences in which the operation of multiplication may be effected, and we think it is an excellent exercise for the reader who is just becoming familiar with the slide rule to work through a few of these sequences. 189 should result from every attempt, and it is a matter of interest to see how little variation there is in the results obtained by taking the factors in different orders. With a little care the reader will find the correct result emerging time after time.

The student may like to know how the 24 sequences referred to are derived. Let us for ease of expression denote the four factors by the letters a, b, c and d. Here are six different sequences: $a \times b \times c \times d$, $a \times b \times d \times c$, $a \times c \times b \times d$, $a \times c \times d \times b$, $a \times d \times b \times c$, $a \times d \times c \times b$. Each of these six starts with a. Now there are six others each starting with b, and similarly six commencing with c and with d. You will, no doubt, be able to complete the whole of the series without difficulty. We are not suggesting the example need be solved in all 24 ways, but to carry out a few will serve as good practice.

Problem 10. A certain material costs £8·50 per m³; calculate the cost to fill a container with the following dimensions: length 5·5 m, breadth 2·25 m, depth 6 m.

Example: Calculate the area of a circle 28 mm radius. (If r is the radius of a circle, and d its diameter, then

$$\text{area} = \pi r^2 = \frac{\pi d^2}{4}.$$ π, pronounced pi, is the Greek

letter which is always used to denote the value 3·14. It is the ratio of circumference to diameter of a circle, and it enters into all our calculations concerning circles, spheres and other associated forms. π is generally denoted by a special "gauge mark" in scales C and D, see Fig. 8.)

$$\text{Area} = \pi(28)^2 = \pi \times 28 \times 28.$$

To 28D set 1C. X to 28C. 10C to X. Result 246 in D under π in C.

Approximation: $3 \times 30 \times 30 = 2700$. Result is 2460 mm².

Problem 11. Calculate the volume of a cylinder 8·2 m radius and 12·6 m long. (Volume $= (\pi r^2) L$.)

Division

If you have now understood the rules for multiplication of two or more factors, you should have no difficulty in using your slide rule for dividing. We will, however, consider a few examples in order to make sure.

If your rule is set to multiply together two numbers, then it is also set for division. Will you adjust the slide so that the 1 in scale C is coincident with 2·5 of scale D. Immediately under the 3 of C you will find 7·5 in D. This setting of the slide enables us to multiply 2·5 by 3. Now, working backwards from this result, we see that in order to divide 7·5 by 3 we need only adjust the slide to bring the 3 of scale C opposite the 7·5 of scale D; exactly under the 1 of C we find the 2·5 of D, and we have effected the division of 7·5 by 3 and obtained the result 2·5.

We repeat our advice: if in doubt concerning method, work out an easy case with simple figures so that a mental check can be obtained easily, such as the following:

Example: How long will it take a man walking at $6\frac{1}{2}$ km/h to cover 26 km? To 26D set 6·5C; and under 10C read 4D; the answer is, therefore, 4 hours.

Please note that henceforward we shall often write the significant figures to be selected in the scales without inserting the decimal points. For example, the numbers 14 and 18 in scale D are those marked 1·4 and 1·8. We hope by now the reader has appreciated that we take no notice of the positions of the decimal points in the various numbers while we are manipulating the slide rule. When we have obtained a numerical result we insert the decimal point by inspection if the numbers are simple; if the numbers are too complicated to allow of a mental approximation to be made, we shall write them down, then simplify and cancel them sufficiently to enable us to obtain an approximate result.

Example: Find the radius of a circle which has an area of 161 m².

$$\text{Now } \pi r^2 = 161. \quad r^2 = \frac{161}{\pi}.$$

To 161D set π in C. Under 10C read 512. Insert decimal point by inspection giving $51 \cdot 2 = r^2$. To obtain the radius we must find the square root of 51·2. There are several ways of finding square roots by slide rule, but remember we are restricted in this section to the use of scales C and D only. We can easily obtain our result: Place X over 51·2 in D and move the slide to bring 7 in C under X. $(7 \times 7 = 49,$ and it is clear that our square root is a little greater than 7.) Now move the slide slowly to the left until the reading in C under X is the same as the reading in D under the 10 in C. We make the answer 7·15.

You will see that our endeavour has been to set the slide so that we are multiplying a number by itself and obtaining 51·2 as the result. Please study very carefully this method of obtaining square root.

Problem 12. A sample of coal weighing 13·4 grammes on analysis was found to contain 9·6 grammes of carbon. Calculate the percentage of carbon contained in the sample.

Example: Find the value of $\dfrac{182}{6 \cdot 2 \times 808 \times \cdot 029}$.

To 182D set 62C; X to 10C; 808C to X; X to 10C; 29C to X. Answer 1252 in D under 1C.

To find the position of the decimal point we may write the expression in a simpler form $\dfrac{182}{6 \cdot 2 \times 8 \cdot 08 \times 2 \cdot 9}$.

You will notice that we have moved the decimal point in the 808 two places to the left. This is equivalent to dividing 808 by 100 and reducing it to 8·08. At the same time we have multiplied the ·029 by 100 by moving the decimal point two places to the right. Now, in an expression such as we are dealing with, we do not alter its numerical value if we multiply and divide the denominator (or numerator) by 100, or any other number, but by this device we alter the terms of the expression in such a manner that we can more easily see the order of the result. If you now look at the denominator you will see that we have approximately $6 \times 8 = 48$, and $48 \times 2 \cdot 9$ is somewhat less than 150. 150 divided into 182 is clearly greater than 1 and less than 2. Our result is, therefore, 1·252.

Multiplication and Division Combined

Frequently calculations involve a combination of multiplication and division. We shall find that our slide rule is particularly well designed to cope with them.

First consider the simple case $\dfrac{8 \times 3}{4}$. We can easily obtain the answer mentally as 6. Using the slide rule we might multiply 8 by 3 and then divide by 4. Alternatively, we might divide the 8 by 4 and then multiply by 3. The answer would be 6 by either method, but we shall find that there are less slide rule operations if we adopt the second.

By first method: To 8D set 10C, X to 3C, 4C to X; under 10C read answer 6 in D.

Second method: To 8D set 4C; under 3C read answer 6 in D.

The first method involves us in four slide rule operations,

whereas the second method demands only two. *You are particularly advised to cultivate the habit of using the second method in all calculations which involve combined multiplications and division.* Compared with the first method you will in general reduce the number of operations by about one-half, and you will often be nearer the exact result.

A little thought will show how the saving is effected. Please set your rule so that 8D is under 4C. This is the setting for dividing 8 by 4 and the answer, 2, is in D immediately under 1 in C. Now, to multiply 2 by 3 we must set the 1 of C to the 2 of D and read the answer, 6, in D under the 3 in C. We find, however, that having set the slide for dividing 8 by 4 we have also, with the same setting, prepared for the multiplication of 2 by 3. We do not even take the trouble to read the intermediate answer, 2, but go direct to the final one, 6.

Example: A farmer is asked to make for a Government Department a return, showing as percentages the areas he has under wheat, oats, barley, root crops, grass and fallow. After a check up he finds that he has sown wheat 375 hectares, oats 290 hectares, barley 175 hectares, root crops 420 hectares, has grass 195 hectares and lying fallow 75 hectares. Total area area is 1530 hectares.

We could divide each of the separate areas by 153 and so obtain the percentages, but we find it much easier first to divide 1 by 153 and then to effect the multiplications with one setting of the slide.

To 1D set 153C, then
under 375C read in D 24·5% wheat
   ,,   290C   ,,   ,, D 19·0% oats
   ,,   175C   ,,   ,, D 11·5% barley
   ,,   420C   ,,   ,, D 27·5% roots
   ,,   195C   ,,   ,, D 12·8% grass
   ,,   75C   ,,   ,, D 4·9% fallow

      Total   100·2%

If we have made our calculations correctly, the total of the crop percentages will be 100%. As you see, our individual percentages give 100·2% as the total. The slight discrepancy is due to the small errors we make when using a slide rule, but the total is so close to 100% that we may assume we have made no error of importance and we need not check through the calculations. If you try to read the percentages to the second place of decimals, you will probably get results which are even nearer to the 100%, but it is futile to express your slide rule result to a degree of accuracy greater than that of the original data. It is quite certain that the farmer's estimation of acreage under the different crops will contain errors much greater than 2 in 1000.

We think the foregoing example gives excellent practice, and we give a similar one for the reader to work through.

Problem 13. The manufacturing costs of a certain article were estimated as follows: Direct Labour £62·50, Drawing Office £10, Materials £77·50, Works Overheads £70, General Overheads £30. Express these items as percentages of the total cost.

We will finish this dissertation with a typical example of combined multiplication and division, since this type of problem arises very frequently in the course of practical work.

$$\textbf{Example:} \quad \frac{8·2 \times 14 \times 7 \times 29·1 \times 77·6 \times 50·2}{18·6 \times 32·7 \times ·606 \times 480}.$$

Set X to 82D, 186C to X, X to 147C, 327C to X, X to 291C, 606C to X, X to 776C, 480C to X, X to 502C.

Read the result 772 in D under X.

Approximation gives 70; therefore, result is 77·2.

Position of the Decimal Point

We have stated earlier in this section that we would give rules for the determination of decimal points in numerical results. In many cases the positions of decimal points are known from the nature of the problem; in many others the decimal point may be inserted by making mentally rough approximations. In cases in which the figures are so numerous and diverse that it is unsafe to attempt to approximate mentally, the data should be written down in round numbers and then reduced to simple forms by cancellation and other means, so that approximation can be made.

Our advice to the reader always to fix the position of decimal points by inspection or approximation is, we believe, quite sound; in the course of a long acquaintance with slide rules and users of slide rules, we have met only one individual who consistently adopted any other method. (If the reader is not interested in the mechanical method of determining the position of the decimal point, he may safely skip the next five or so pages and read on at "Additional Examples".)

Digits

When we speak of the number of digits in a factor we refer to the number of figures lying before the decimal point when the factor is 1 or more. When the factor is less than 1, the number of digits is the number of noughts immediately following the decimal point, and this number of digits is negative. In the following factors given as examples, the numbers of digits are given in brackets: 6 (1); 81 (2); 508 (3); ·45 (0); ·026 (−1); ·0048 (−2); ·0007 (−3).

Rule for Multiplication

Please set your rule for multiplying 3 by 4. The result is 12, and the slide is protruding at the left-hand end of the stock. In this example the number of digits in the product is 2, which is equal to the sum of the digits of the two factors which contain one each.

The following examples in which 3 and 4 are the significant figures show how the index rule works. In each case you will see the sum of the digits (which are shown in brackets) of the two factors is equal to the digits in the product.

·3 (0) × 4 (1) = 1·2 (1).   400 (3) × 3000 (4) = 1,200,000 (7).
·03 (−1) × ·004 (−2) = ·00012 (−3).

Now if you will set the rule for multiplication of 2 by 4, the slide will protrude at the right-hand end of the stock. In this case the sum of the digits of the two factors is 2, whereas there is only one digit in the product.

The rule for a product which emerges from these simple examples, and which is true for all, is:

> If the rule is set with the slide protruding at the left-hand end of the stock, the number of digits in the answer is the sum of the digits of the factors. If the slide is protruding at the right-hand end, the number of digits in the product is one less than the sum of the digits of the factors.

Example: Multiply 61·3 × ·008 × ·24 × 9·19 × 18·6.

> There are four settings of slide necessary, and we shall find that in three the slide protrudes to the left, and in one to the right. We must, therefore, find the sum of the digits of the five factors and subtract 1, shown in the square bracket, i.e. 2 − 2 + 0 + 1 + 2 − [1] = 2. The final reading in scale D is 201, the result is 20·1.

Problem 14. Multiply ·068 × 1200 × 1·68 × ·00046 × 28·3.

Rule for Division

If you have understood the rule for multiplication you will have no difficulty with the corresponding rule for division, which may now be stated:

> If, when dividing, the slide protrudes at the left-hand end of the stock, the number of digits in the result is found by subtracting the number of digits in the divisor from the number in the dividend. If the slide protrudes to the right,

the number of digits in the result will be one greater than the difference between the numbers of digits in the dividend and divisor respectively.

Example: $\dfrac{6\cdot1}{128\times\cdot039\times18}.$

To 61D set 128C Slide to right Digit adjustment $+1$
X to 1C
39C to X   ,,   ,,   ,,   ,, $+1$
X to 1C
18C to X   Slide to left   ,,   ,,   0

Result 679 in D under 10C.

Since the slide protruded twice at the right-hand end, we must add 2 to the number of digits derived from the factors.

Digits in answer $=1-3-(-1)-2+[2]$
$=1-3+1-2+2=-1.$

Result is $\cdot0679$.

Problem 15. Evaluate $\dfrac{864}{917\times\cdot0028\times46\cdot1\times8\cdot9}.$

Example: Let us now examine an example such as the

$$\frac{2\times3\times4}{1\cdot5\times8}.$$

We can see at a glance that the answer is 2, since the $1\cdot5\times8$ in the denominator cancels with the 3×4 in the numerator, leaving only the 2 as the result.

If you will use your slide rule to find this result, you will see that commencing with the 2 you can divide by 15 and multiply by 3 with one setting of the slide, and then divide by 8 and multiply by 4 with another setting of the slide. When it is possible to carry out two operations at one slide setting you may disregard the position of the slide, i.e. whether to right hand or left hand of the stock, since if digits have to be added or subtracted they will be equal and of opposite signs, and will consequently cancel out. It is only when the slide protrudes to the right and either multiplication or division is effected separately that the number of digits in the result is affected.

We will write down the operations involved in this simple exercise:

Set 15C to 2D	Slide to right	Digit adjustment		+1
Set X to 3C	,, ,,	,,	,,	−1
Set 8C to X	Slide to left	,,	,,	0
Result 2 in D under 4C	Slide to left	,,	,,	0

The first and second operations are performed at one setting of the slide. They represent division by 15 followed by multiplication by 3. The slide protrudes to the right hand of the stock, and if we consider these two operations as quite distinct from one another the digit adjustment will be +1 for the division and −1 for the multiplication. These cancel one another. In the third and fourth operation, since the slide protrudes to the left-hand end, the digit adjustment is 0 in either case. You will see, therefore, that in cases of combined multiplication and division you can reduce the check, on the digits to be added or deducted, if you select the factors so that two operations may be performed with the single setting of the slide as often as possible.

Example: Find the value of the following expression:

$$\frac{8 \cdot 1 \times 143 \times \cdot 0366 \times 92 \cdot 8 \times 238}{62 \times 188 \times \cdot 450 \times 85 \cdot 5}.$$

We will first multiply the five factors in the numerator and follow with the divisions by the four factors in the denominator.

Under 81D

set 10C	Slide to left	Digit adjustment	0
X to 143C			
1C to X	,, ,,	,, ,,	−1
X to 366C			
10C to X	,, left	,, ,,	0
X to 928C			
1C to X	,, right	,, ,,	−1
X to 238			
62C to X	,, right	,, ,,	+1
X to 1C			
188C to X	,, left	,, ,,	0
X to 10C			
45C to 2X	,, right	,, ,,	+1
X to 1C			
85·5C to X	,, left	,, ,,	0

Result 209 in D under 10C.   Total   0

Digits in numerator $=1+3-1+2+3=8$

,,   denominator$=2+3+0+2$ $=7$

Diff.   1

Collecting the digits gives a total of 1 from the two sources, therefore the answer is 2·09.

Let us re-work this example by dividing and multiplying alternately to see if the digits rule gives the same result.

To 81D set 62C	Slide to right	Digit adjustment	0
X to 143C	,, ,,		
188C to X	,, left	,, ,,	
X to 366C	,, ,,		
45C to X	,, left	,, ,,	
X to 928C	,, ,,		
85·5C to X	,, ,,	,, ,,	
Result 209D under 238C	,, ,,		

Take note of the great saving in manipulation of the rule, as compared with doing all the multiplication first and the division afterwards. The digit adjustment is 0 and the result is still the same, 2·09. The operations bracketed together in pairs are those which are effected at one setting of the slide. The first operation of each pair is always a division effected by setting the slide, and the second a multiplication, made by moving the cursor.

As an exercise we suggest you work through the problem for a third time by dividing and multiplying alternately, but taking the factors in a different order from that which we have adopted above. The result is quite independent of the order selected, and the digit rule will give the same position for the decimal point.

We leave the decision to you whether you will use these rules for fixing the position of the decimal point or adopt the approximation method. Apart from slide rule considerations, you will find that to develop the faculty for making quick approximate estimations is useful in many other ways. In a long computation there is a risk that we may overlook a factor and omit it from our slide rule calculation. The chance of doing this is perhaps not great, but if we have several factors in both numerator and denominator we try to select them in pairs, one in the denominator and one in the numerator, so that we can use them together in one setting of the slide, and, further, we try to select a pair of factors which are near to one another in values, so that the movement of the cursor is small. Now, in making selection of factors to best suit the manipulation of the slide rule lies the risk of omitting a factor. If we subsequently make an approximation to fix the position of decimal point, the omission of a factor will be disclosed.

Additional Examples

We mentioned earlier that we regard the C and D scales as most important in the early stages of our acquaintance with the slide rule. We therefore now give some additional examples, graded in difficulty, illustrating the use of these scales. The solutions are given in each case, but we recommend the reader to work these examples independently and to refer to the solutions only when in doubt. He will understand that there are alternative ways of selecting the various factors involved and he should repeat some of the examples by using different sequences of operations.

Example: A cycle journey of 437 kilometres occupies $8\frac{1}{4}$ hours. What is the average speed?

To 437D set 825C.

Under 10C read 53 (53 km/h).

Example: A student obtained $47\frac{1}{2}$ marks out of a possible 78. What is the percentage marks obtained?

To 475D set 78C.

Read 609D under 10C (60·9%).

Example: A group of students obtained the following numbers of marks, in all cases out of a possible 78. Calculate the percentages. $47\frac{1}{2}$, 63, $51\frac{1}{2}$, 72, 65, 23, $37\frac{1}{2}$.

To 10D, set 78C.

Read 609D under 475C (60·9%).
,,   808D   ,,   63C (80·8%).
,,   66D   ,,   515C (66%).
,,   923D   ,,   72C (92·3%).
,,   833D   ,,   65C (83·3%).
,,   295D   ,,   23C (29·5%).
,,   482D   ,,   375C (48·2%).

(This present example is a good illustration of how we can use a slide rule without any prior knowledge of the instrument, of mathematics, of logarithms or of any other feature; all that is necessary is the ability to read the scales in the same way as one reads, say, a thermometer scale. What we are doing in effec is to set 78 against 100% saying "In this sum, 78 marks = 100%". At a glance we can see that 39 marks represent 50%, and this means that we can pick up any figure representing marks between 10 and 78 marks, reading against it the percentage involved. It happens in this example that no student obtained as few as 8 or 9 marks; if either of these two figures had existed then in order to produce the percentage we would have had to "traverse the slide", as referred to previously. This example provides such a good case of the simplest use of a slide rule that we have broken off with these few remarks in case the reader may feel that this example would be a good one to demonstrate his prowess to friends, colleagues or relatives, etc.)

The reader will note that, if only one percentage is required, it is best to divide the marks obtained by the marks possible. If a series of results is to be dealt with, it is much quicker to proceed as indicated in this example.

Example: Calculate the cost of material 10·5 m long by 3·5 m diameter at $62·30 per m³.

This computation is

$$\frac{\pi}{4} (3 \cdot 5)^2 \times 10 \cdot 5 \times 623.$$

To 35D set 4C
    X to 35C
    1C to X
    X to πC
    10C to X
    X to 105C
    1C to X.

Under 623C read 63D ($6300). *Approximation*: $3\frac{1}{2}$ squared is about 12, dividing by 4 gives 3 and $3 \times \pi$ is nearly 10. We have then $10 \times 10 = 100$ times

62 is 6200. In this example you may shorten the work by squaring $3\frac{1}{2}$ mentally. $(\frac{7}{2})^2 = \frac{49}{4}$ and combining the 4 under the π we start with $\pi \times \frac{49}{16} \times 10\cdot5 \times 62\cdot3$. This idea of reducing the factors is valuable provided the mental operations are simple. It is a habit all slide rule users soon acquire.

Example: A job takes $8\frac{1}{2}$ days to complete by 19 men working $12\frac{1}{2}$ hours per day. How long would the same job take if the number of men is increased to 23 and the working day reduced to 8 hours?

Result is obtained from $8\frac{1}{2} \times \dfrac{19}{23} \times \dfrac{12\frac{1}{2}}{8}$.

To 85D set 23C
    X to 19C
    8C to X.

Read 10·9D under 125C (11 days).

Example: Compute $\dfrac{4\cdot2 \times 71 \times 6\cdot76 \times \cdot382}{7\cdot24 \times 2\cdot5 \times \cdot855}$.

This example is typical of a large range of problems which give rise to a string of figures which has to be reduced to a numerical answer. The reader will notice no useful cancellation can be made, nor is it possible to combine any of the factors mentally. The result can quickly be obtained by combined multiplication and division. A check on the result should be obtained by repeating the slide rule manipulation with alternative factor sequences. In the solution below the factors have been selected in such a manner that the movements of cursor have been reduced to a minimum. This is a desirable practice and should be cultivated by the student.

To 42D set 724C
    X to 71C
    25C to X

X to 382C
855C to X.

Read 498D under 676C.

Result is 49·8, the decimal point being fixed by approximate cancellation.

A AND B SCALES

WITHOUT doubt the most frequently used scales of the standard slide rule are the C and D scales we have just studied, and we might, with justification, say that these are the most important scales in our slide rule equipment. It is impossible to say which scales stand next in importance. It depends upon the nature of the work to be done; if trigonometrical problems loom prominently in our work, then the sin and tan scales will frequently be used. Work of a different nature may demand frequent recourse to the log-log scale, and again electrical or commercial calculations may bring into service scales particularly designed to deal with them.

The reader will notice that we do not suggest the A and B scales possess a high degree of priority in the scheme of things. We are of the opinion that these scales are of little importance and that others could, with advantage, be substituted for them.

Since, however, the large majority of slide rules are equipped with A and B scales, we must spend a little time in studying them.

The A and B scales are adjacent to one another, the B scale lying along the top edge of the slide and the A scale on the stock. The reader will see them in Figs. 6 and 7. Each of these scales consists, so far as its graduations are concerned, of two identical halves, and we speak of the right-hand half, or the left-hand half, when we desire to make a distinction.

Scales A and B should carry 1 at the extreme left-hand end, 10 at the middle point where the two halves abut and finish with 100 at the right-hand end, with the corresponding intermediate figures. In many slide rules the left-hand and right-hand halves are numbered exactly alike, with the figure 1 at the beginning and end of each half. Whilst this arrangement is not a great disadvantage to those familiar with slide rules, and expert in the use of them, we think the scale should be completely numbered as shown in Fig. 7. In subsequent notes we shall refer to the numbers as they are depicted in Fig. 7.

Each half of scales A or B is similar to scales C and D inasmuch as it is logarithmic. It is only half the length, and has only about half the graduations, and herein lies the disadvantage of using A and B for multiplication or division.

The reader is by now quite well aware that a slide rule will not give results with absolute accuracy. If we multiply together two numbers using ordinary arithmetical procedure we should obtain a result accurate to the last figure, but with a 250 mm slide rule we know that we can never be certain of the fourth figure and must often regard the third figure with suspicion. A 125 mm rule is less precise, and if one uses the A and B scales of a 250 mm rule for ordinary multiplication or division one is in effect using a 125 mm rule. We have heard sarcastic criticism of the slide rule arising from the fact that results are not always completely accurate, but the thoughtful reader will, of course, realise that in our practical problems the data we use are derived generally from measurements or observations which are susceptible to considerable error, in comparison with which the errors made in computation by slide rule are permissible.

We would, however, warn the reader carefully to consider whether the slide rule is likely to introduce errors which might seriously impair the result of some work or investigation he is pursuing. In the course of a chemical analysis, we might, using a good balance, determine the weight of a sample as 13·562 grammes, and we should be fairly certain that the last figure, the 2, was correct, and not 1 or 3. If this weight had to be multiplied by some other number which could equally be relied upon, we should hesitate at using a 250 mm slide rule, which might introduce an error many times as great as any error in the original figures. Some physical measurements can be made to a high degree of accuracy, and computations must, of course, be made with the same precision. When necessary we must discard the slide rule and use other means of reaching the result, but for most of our practical work the C and D scales of a 250 mm slide rule give results to an acceptable degree of accuracy.

When great accuracy of results is not important, and we are working to approximate figures, there is no harm in using scales A and B for multiplication and division, but we do ask the reader to avoid making this a practice, or he will soon find himself by habit using A and B when he should be working with C and D.

With very little modification, the instructions we have given in respect of scales C and D for multiplication and division apply to A and B. For scale D read A, for C read B, and remember that due to the duplication of the scales all the numbers in C and D appear twice in A and B, e.g. the 2 in C and D appears as 2 and 20 in A and B.

We have seen that when using C and D it occasionally happens that after carefully setting the slide we find that the next factor is "off the scale", and the slide has to be moved its own length and then re-set to obtain the required reading. When we use scales A and B, we find that, if a factor in scale B is off the A scale at one end of the rule, the result can still be found by looking for the factor in the other half of scale B. It *is* possible to set the slide so that no result can be found. To avoid this, refrain from moving the slide so that more than half its length protrudes from the stock, remembering there are two alternative settings. Cultivate the habit when setting the slide of keeping it near the centre of the stock. It is natural to do this, and if persisted in for a time becomes a habit. We do not propose to say anything further concerning multiplication and division with scales A and B.

Squares and Square Roots

In Section 3 we mentioned that squares and square roots of numbers are easily obtained by using scales A and D in conjunction, and this, we suggest, is the most useful feature arising from the inclusion of scales A and B in our slide rule.

Immediately above any number in scale D appears its square in scale A. Look at your slide rule and you will find 4 in A over 2 in D, 9 in A over 3 in D, 25 in A over 5 in D, and similarly throughout the length of the scales. Conversely, the square roots of numbers in A lie directly below in D. When projecting from A to D or vice versa, we may use the cursor index line or, if preferred, the index lines of the slide. The index lines of the slide are the end lines (excluding extensions if any), the 1 and 100 of scale B, and 1 and 10 of C. It will be clear that these lines give a means of striking across from A to D, and sometimes these are preferred to the cursor index, since there is no possibility of slight error due to parallax.

The student will find no difficulty in squaring numbers:

Example: Find the square of 4·55.

Set X to 455D. Under X read 207 in A. Result 20·7.

If we use the slide to project across the rule, the procedure is:

Set 10C to 455D. Read result 20·7 in A over 100B.

We shall, in subsequent notes, refer to X, the cursor index or projecting from A to D, but we advise the reader to use the slide when it is convenient to do so. In many calculations involving squares and square roots, the slide cannot be used for projecting across, since it is required for other operations. In such cases the X must be employed.

Problem 16. Find the squares of 8·75 and 167.

Evaluation of square roots is the reverse operation and is just as easy, but there is one point we must mention in passing.

If using scales A and B we desire to multiply 2 by some other factor, we may use the 2 in the left-hand half of A, or the 20 in the right-hand half, taking the figure most convenient, but if we require the square root of 2 we may not use the 20. The reader will see that under 2 of A the reading in D is 1·414, whereas under 20 in A appears 4·47 in D. We know of no more prolific source of slide rule error than this one of using the wrong half of scale A when extracting square roots.

There should be no difficulty in finding the square root of any number lying between 1 and 100. We know the square roots of 1, 4, 9, 16, 25, 36, 49, 64, 81 and 100, and we should make no mistake with any number within this range.

Assume we require the square root of 45·2. We place X over 452 in the left-hand half of A and note the corresponding value in D; it is 213. The square root of 49 is 7 and our answer should be just less than 7. 213 does not agree, and we see immediately that we have in error taken the square root of 4·52, which is 2·13. If we move the cursor to 452 in the right-hand half of scale A, we find the corresponding reading in D is 6·72; this is the square root of 45·2.

If the scales of your slide rule are comprehensively numbered, as in Fig. 7, the problem of extracting square roots is simplified, since there will be no difficulty with numbers lying between 1 and 100. When extracting square roots, it is advisable to multiply or divide the original number by even powers of 10 to bring it into the range of 1 to 100 and, after taking the square root, to make the necessary adjustment in the result.

Examples: Find the square roots of (i) 1462; (ii) ·0000227 and (iii) ·000227.

(i) $\sqrt{1462} = \sqrt{14·62 \times 100} = \sqrt{14·62} \times 10 = 3·82 \times 10 = 38·2.$

(ii) Starting with ·0000227, we tick off pairs of figures as shown ·00′00′22′7; we thus obtain 22·7 as the figure whose square root we must find on the slide rule. This root is 4·76, but we must now move the decimal point three places to the left to correct the alteration made when earlier we ticked off three pairs of figures to the right.

Result is ·00476.

(iii) $\sqrt{\cdot 00'02'27}$

$\sqrt{2\cdot 27} = 1\cdot 505.$ Result $\cdot 01505.$

We could give the reader other rules for the determination of position of decimal point in the root, but we are confident that the method we have adopted above is the best. It is easily understood, but because of its importance we will enumerate the steps:

(1) Examine the number whose square root is required. If it lies between 1 and 100 its square root will lie between 1 and 10. Find the number in A and project with X to D where the root will be found. Insert the decimal point to the right of the first figure of the result.

(2) If the number does not lie between 1 and 100 move the decimal point in steps of two figures at a time until the number falls in this range; now take the square root of the number so altered and insert the decimal point as at (1) above.

(3) Finally, move the decimal point in the result obtained at (2), one place for each step of two figures made when altering the number, moving in the opposite direction.

Problem 17. Find the square roots of 814, 8140, $\cdot 0166$ and $\cdot 0000166.$

Example: Calculate the volume of a cylinder $11\cdot 2$ m diameter, $19\cdot 6$ m long.

In terms of diameter d and length l the volume is

$$\frac{\pi}{4} d^2 l.$$

Find 112D and set 1C over it, X to 196B, 10B to X

Result 193 in A above 785B. $\left(\cdot 785 = \dfrac{\pi}{4} \right).$

Approximation: $11 \times 11 = 132.$ $\frac{3}{4}$ of 132 is near 100. $100 \times 19\cdot 6 = 1960.$

Result 1930 m².

Find the cost represented by this volume at 51p
per m³. X at 193A, place 1B under X above 51B,
read answer 984 in A or £984·00.

The symbols c and c' which appear in some slide rules near
the left-hand end and near the middle of the C scale are
provided to assist in calculations involving volumes of cylinders. The special lines are termed gauge points; they are
referred to in Section 15.

Problem 18. Calculate the area of a circular carpet 21·1 m
across and its weight at 2·82 kg/m².

There are methods of finding square roots without using
scales A and B. We used one in the example preceding
Problem 4. Other methods will be mentioned in the sections
dealing with log-log and reciprocal scales.

Cubes and Cube Roots

To find the cube of any number set the 1 or 10 of scale C
to the number in D. Above the number in B read the cube
in A.

Example: Find the cube of 2·44.

To 244D set 1C. Over 244 in B, read in A the cube,
which is 145. Insert the decimal point by inspection,
making the answer 14·5.

There are rules which may be used for the determination of
the position of the decimal point in the result, but they are
confusing, and we cannot recommend the reader to use them.
It is simpler to obtain an approximate result.

Problem 19. Cube 16·8.

Cube roots may be extracted by several different methods
using scales A, B, C and D. The method we now describe is
we think, the best.

When extracting square roots we converted the number whose root was required to one lying between 1 and 100. In the case of cube roots we step off figures, in groups of three, until the number whose cube root we are finding lies between 1 and 1000. The cube root will then lie between 1 and 10.

The slide rule manipulation is as follows:

Place the cursor index X over the original number in scale A. Adjust the slide so that the number in scale B under X is exactly the same as the number in D opposite 1 (or 10) of C. The number so found is the cube root.

If the reader will use his slide rule and set X over 8 in A he will find that, when the slide is set so that 2B lies under X, 2D will be opposite 1C, 2 being the cube root of 8.

If the number whose cube root is sought lies between 1 and 100, use the appropriate reading in scale A for setting X, but if the original number lies between 100 and 1000, select it in the left-hand half of A, which, for our present purpose, must be regarded as a continuation of the A scale and stretching from 100 to 1000.

These instructions may seem rather complicated, but if the reader will take his slide rule to find the cube roots of say, 6, 60 and 600, using the 6 in the left-hand part of scale A for the 6 and 600, and the right-hand half of the scale for the 60, he will find no difficulty in reading the three roots, 1·82 in D under 1C, 3·91 in D under 1C and 8·44 in D under 10C.

In extracting cube roots it helps considerably in setting the slide if a mental estimation of the root is made. If we require the cube root of 450, we try, say, 6. $6 \times 6 = 36$, which we call 40; now $6 \times 40 = 240$, and this is well below 450. Try 7; 7 squared is 49, say 50, and $7 \times 50 = 350$. Still too small, so try 8. $8 \times 8 = 64$; and $8 \times 60 = 480$. We have passed the 450, so our cube root lies between figures 7 and 8. We therefore set X to 45 in the right-hand part of scale A and our slide so that 10 in C is near 8D, and if we now move the slide slowly to the left we shall find that when 10C is over 7·66D, X is over 7·66B. ∴ $\sqrt[3]{450} = 7·66$.

Example: Find the cube root of ·000′012′64.

First move the decimal point to the right in steps of three figures, as shown by the ticks, until a number lying between 1 and 1000 is found. This number is 12·64. The cube root of 12 is between 2 and 3. Set X to 12·64 in A. Set 1C to 2D. Now move the slide to the right. When 1C reaches 233D, 233B will be under X. The cube root of 12·64 is 2·33, but we must now move the decimal point two places to the left to compensate for the stepping off of two groups of figures in the original number. The required cube root is ·0233.

Problem 20. Find the cube roots of 8, 80, 800, 9481, ·0213 and ·00046.

Cube Scale

Slide rules equipped with a special scale for evaluating cubes and cube roots of numbers are available. Unless the reader is concerned with work which involves the necessity of frequently finding cubes or cube roots—we cannot think of any work which does—he will find little use for the scale. The cube scale usually lies along the top or bottom edge of the face of the stock, and if the reader will inspect it he will see that the complete scale is made up of three identical scales placed end to end. Each of these three parts is one-third of the length of the C or D scales, and is divided logarithmically. The left-hand third of the scale starts at 1 and finishes at 10, the middle third stretches from 10 to 100 and the right-hand third from 100 to 1000.

To cube a number it is only necessary to project it from scale D to the cube scale, and cube roots are found by projecting numbers from the cube scale to the D scale.

After reading the instructions we have given for extracting cube roots by the A, B, C and D scales, the reader should have no difficulty when he is using a rule with a scale of cubes. The stepping off of groups of three figures to bring the origina number within the limits of 1 and 1000 should be effected. This makes it easy to select the number in the appropriate section of the cube scale. After the cube root is found in D, the adjustment of the position of the decimal point follows the rules we have given earlier.

LOG-LOG SCALES

ASSOCIATED with slide rules, we occasionally see quite unfamiliar scales which have been evolved for special purposes by people who have many calculations of a peculiar nature to make. If a complete collection of such special scales could be made, it would, no doubt, furnish an interesting study, and occasionally surprise on account of its diversity.

Log-log scales are less frequently used than the scales we have so far studied, but they are not in any sense "special" scales. Many people who have possessed a slide rule for years are not familiar with log-log scales, since these are not included in the scale equipment of the standard slide rule.

Popular models of inexpensive slide rules sold in large quantities in this country include log-log scales and, as there are now a very large number of these rules in use, it may be assumed that the use of the log-log scales is extending. Apart from considerations of utility, the inclusion of log-log scales adds to the pleasure which may be derived from the use of a slide rule.

In Section 13 we shall see that in order to raise a quantity to a power or to extract a root we must look out the logarithm of the quantity, then multiply by the index and so obtain the logarithm of the result. The evaluation of $5 \cdot 6^{1 \cdot 8}$ involves finding the log of $5 \cdot 6$, multiplying it by $1 \cdot 8$. This gives the log of the answer, i.e. $(\log 5 \cdot 6) \times 1 \cdot 8 = \log$ of answer. We cannot perform these operations entirely with the ordinary scales since we must consult a table of logarithms. (It is true that if a slide rule is equipped with a log scale—which must not be confused with the log-log scale—we can find the log of a quantity and, after multiplying by the index, find the anti-log of the product, and so obtain the result, Regarded from practical standpoint, the slide rule is used to save time, and on these grounds there is nothing to be gained by using the log scale in preference to a table of logs; the latter is certainly more accurate.)

If we have a means of finding the log of (log 5·6) we can proceed thus: log (log 5·6) + log 1·8 = log (log answer).

As its name signifies, the log-log scale is designed so that its graduations represent values of the logarithms of logarithms of numbers; the graduations of the ordinary scale represent logarithms of numbers.

It is important to understand that the numbers marked along a log-log scale cannot be varied. We know that the 2 in the C or D scales may be used as 2 or 20 or 2000 or ·0002, but the number 2 in the log-log scale can have no other value except 2. The reader will, therefore, realise that the range of the log-log scale selected for use in any rule is fixed and limited. It is for the designer of the slide rule to decide what is the best range to include in any particular type of rule.

The log-log scale frequently lies along the top and bottom edges of the face of the stock, and if the reader will examine Fig. 7 he will see that the scale lying along the upper edge of the stock starts at 1·1 and finishes at 2·9. The lower scale starts at 2·6 and finishes at 40,000. These two scales are, in fact, one scale only, divided into two parts. The upper portion should be regarded as the part of the complete scale lying in front of the lower section. There are small overlaps on both scales. Strictly speaking, the upper scale finishes at 2·7183, immediately above 10D, and the lower starts at the same value directly under 1D. The log-log scale is used in conjunction with scale C.

As we have said, the limits of the complete scale can be varied, and you may find that the scales of your slide rule, assuming it has a log-log scale, may be different from the one shown in Fig. 7. In some rules you may find more than two sections of log-log scales, but whatever type of rule you possess the examples given below are typical of the calculations which can be made with it.

Evaluation of Powers and Roots

The most useful feature associated with the log-log scale is the ease with which all powers and roots can be calculated. (Abbreviations LU and LL = Upper and Lower log-log scales respectively.)

Example: Evaluate (i) $6 \cdot 4^{2 \cdot 7}$ and (ii) $^{2 \cdot 7}\sqrt{6 \cdot 4}$.

    (i) To $6 \cdot 4$ LL set 1C. X to $2 \cdot 7$C.
        Result under X in LL = 150.

    (ii) To $6 \cdot 4$ LL set $2 \cdot 7$C. X to 10C.
         Result under X in LU = $1 \cdot 99$.

Example: Evaluate $6 \cdot 4^{-2 \cdot 7}$.

$$6 \cdot 4^{-2 \cdot 7} = \frac{1}{6 \cdot 4^{2 \cdot 7}} = \frac{1}{150} \text{ (From Ex. (i) above)} = \cdot 00667.$$

Problem 21. Evaluate $21 \cdot 5^{1 \cdot 66}$; $^{1 \cdot 66}\sqrt{21 \cdot 5}$; $21 \cdot 5^{-1 \cdot 66}$.

Example: Evaluate (i) $21^{4 \cdot 5}$; (ii) $^{9}\sqrt{2}$.

If the reader will attempt to effect these evaluations by the methods adopted in the preceding examples, he will find the answers "off the scale", in both cases. Result can be found quite easily as now shown.

  (i) $21^{4 \cdot 5} = 7^{4 \cdot 5} \times 3^{4 \cdot 5}$ (or the factors $2 \cdot 1$ and 10 might be taken)

        $= 6300 \times 140$ (evaluate separately as first example)

        $= 882000$ (multiplication by C and D scales).

  (ii) $^{9}\sqrt{2} = \frac{^{9}\sqrt{20}}{^{9}\sqrt{10}} = \frac{1 \cdot 395}{1 \cdot 292} = 1 \cdot 08.$

In this example the reader will find that, when the 20 is found in LL and 9C is brought into coincidence with it, the 1C index is off the LL scale. If he imagines the LU scale to lie in front of the LL scale, he will see that 1C would then be directly over 1·395 LU. Actually, the 1·395 LU is found, using X directly over 10C, since in effect we have moved the LU scale from its imaginary position in front of the LL scale a distance to the right equal to the length of the C scale, i.e. 250 mm.

Problem 22. Evaluate $1·2^{80}$ and $\sqrt[3]{1·2}$.

Common Logarithms

The log-log scale gives a means of finding common logarithms. Using X, set 1 of C to 10 in LL and project with X, the number whose log is required, from LU or LL into scale C. The logarithm so found will be complete with characteristic and mantissa. When 10 of C is set to 10LL the result obtained is 10 times the true figure.

Example: Find the common log of 150.

Set 1C to 10LL.

Above 150 in LL read in C 2·178.

Example: Find the common log of 3.

Set 10C to 10LL.

Above 3 in LL read in C 4·77, one tenth of which is 0·477.

The reader will see that the logs to any base may be found in a similar way. The 1C or 10C being set to the base in LL or LU.

Natural Logarithms

If the reader will examine Fig. 7 he will see that the 1 of D lies immediately above 2·7183 (the base of the Naperian system of logarithms) in LL. The scales are positioned so that the natural or Naperian logs of all numbers in the log-log scales appear directly opposite in D. When projecting from LU, however, the result obtained is 10 times the true figure.

Example: Find the natural logs of 1·8 and 250.

Use X to project from 1·8 in LU, and 250 in LL into scale D.

Logs so found are ·588 and 5·51.

We do not recommend that logarithms should be found as above except when other means of finding them are not to hand. Logarithms should be taken from tables. Naperian logs are derived from common logs by multiplying by 2·303.

The tenth powers of all numbers in LU lie immediately below in LL, and the tenth roots of all numbers in LL lie directly above in LU. The reader will appreciate these facts if he remembers that LU and LL together form one continuous scale with LU preceding LL.

Example: Find the tenth power of 21.

21 lies in LL, but 2·1 is in LU, and we can use $2·1 \times 10$ and raise each factor to the tenth power. Projecting 2·1 from LU to LL we obtain 1670, and the result, therefore, is 1670×10^{10}.

Example: Find the tenth root of 200.

Set X to 200 in LL. Read in LU 1·7.

Problem 23. Evaluate $3·2^{10}$ and $\sqrt[10]{13}$.

We do not suggest that tenth powers and roots are likely to be required often in practical work.

Since we can use the log-log scales to evaluate *all* powers and roots, we can find square roots and cube roots by the same means, and frequently with a higher degree of accuracy than when using the A and D scales. The reader will now understand our contention that the A and B scales are of little value in a slide rule equipped with a log-log scale.

Example: Find the square root of 1·28 using (i) scales A and D; (ii) log-log scale.

    (i) Use X or the index lines of the slide to project 1·28A into scale D. The result appears to be a shade greater than 1·13.

    (ii) Set X to 1·28LU, 2C to X, X to 1C. Result 1·1313 under X in LU.

The reader will find scope for the display of his ingenuity in obtaining results which cannot be directly taken from the log-log scales, and we think he will find a good deal of pleasure in using a slide rule equipped with these scales.

The Dualistic rule is dealt with in Section 10. This is equipped with *three*-section log-log scales which are carried on the reverse of the slides. The additional sections of these scales increase the range from 1·01 to 40,000 as against 1·1 to 40,000 of the two-section LL scales.

If the reader has comprehended the explanation given above in respect of log-log calculations, he will have no difficulty with a slide rule which has its LL scale on the back of the slide. He will find an explanatory note, under reference log-log scales, in Section 10.

BASIC TRIGONOMETRY

Introduction

IF a man sets out walking in a direction 30° N. of E., it is possible, by means of a simple scale drawing, to show how far

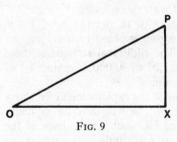

FIG. 9

N. and how far E. he has moved after walking a total of 200 m. Fig. 9, which is to scale, shows these distances to be 100 m (XP) and 173 m (OX) respectively.

Had the distance moved been 250 m, the same diagram could have been used, but it would have represented a different scale. The distance moved North would have been 125 m. Whatever the value of OP the value of XP would always be $OP/2$ if the direction was the same:

i.e. $\dfrac{OP}{XP} = 2$ whatever the value of OP, so long as the angle $POX = 30°$.

Trigonometry is essentially concerned with the relationships between the sides of triangles and the angles they subtend. A knowledge of these relationships is particularly useful in, for example, surveying.

The Right-angled Triangle

Initially we shall confine ourselves to a simple triangle with a right angle, as illustrated in Fig. 10. Following standard convention, the vertices, and the angles at the vertices, are labelled with capital letters, and the sides opposite these angles are denoted by small letters.

The side opposite the right angle is called the *hypotenuse*. In this triangle the hypotenuse is b.

If we are referring to angle C,

side "c" is called the "*opposite*",

side "a" is called the "*adjacent*".

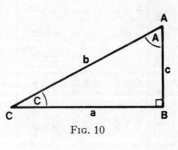

FIG. 10

Relative to angle A, of course, side a would be the opposite and side c the adjacent.

The ratio $\dfrac{\textbf{Opposite}}{\textbf{Hypotenuse}}$ is called the **Sine** (abbrev. = sin) of the angle concerned.

Thus $$\sin C = \frac{c}{b}.$$

For a given value of C the ratio is always the same, *whatever* the actual value of b. The larger b becomes, the larger must be the corresponding value of c.

Similarly, $\dfrac{\textbf{Adjacent}}{\textbf{Hypotenuse}}$ is called the **Cosine** (abbrev. = cos) of the angle,

i.e. $$\cos C = \frac{a}{b}$$

and

$\dfrac{\textbf{Opposite}}{\textbf{Adjacent}}$ is called the **Tangent** (abbrev. = tan) of the angle,

i.e. $$\tan C = \frac{c}{a}.$$

Sines

Degrees	0	1	2	3	4	5	6	7	8	9	10'	20'	30'	40'	50'
0	0·000	017	035	052	070	087	105	122	139	156	3	6	9	12	14
10	0·174	191	208	225	242	259	276	292	309	326	3	6	8	11	14
20	0·342	358	375	391	407	423	438	454	469	485	3	5	8	11	13
30	0·500	515	530	545	559	574	588	602	616	629	2	5	7	10	12
40	0·643	656	669	682	695	707	719	731	743	755	2	4	6	8	10
50	0·766	777	788	799	809	819	829	839	848	857	2	3	5	7	8
60	0·866	875	883	891	899	906	914	920	927	934	1	3	4	5	6
70	0·940	946	951	956	961	966	970	974	978	982	1	2	2	3	4
80	0·985	988	990	993	995	996	998	999	0·999	1·000	0	0	1	1	1

Tangents

Degrees	0	1	2	3	4	5	6	7	8	9	10'	20'	30'	40'	50'
0	0·000	017	035	052	070	087	105	123	141	158	3	6	9	12	15
10	0·176	194	213	231	249	268	287	306	325	344	3	6	9	13	16
20	0·364	384	404	424	445	466	488	510	532	554	4	7	11	14	18
30	0·577	601	625	649	674	700	727	754	781	810	4	9	13	17	22
40	0·839	0·869	0·900	0·933	0·966	1·000	1·036	1·072	1·111	1·150	6	12	18	24	29
50	1·19	1·23	1·28	1·33	1·38	1·43	1·48	1·54	1·60	1·66	1	2	3	4	4
60	1·73	1·80	1·88	1·96	2·05	2·14	2·25	2·36	2·48	2·61	2	3	5	7	8
70	2·75	2·90	3·08	3·27	3·49	3·73	4·01	4·33	4·70	5·14					m.d. cease to be suff. accurate
80						11·43	14·30	19·08	28·64	57·29					

It is comparatively easy to find the values of these ratios for different angles by means of a protractor and scale diagrams, but the most usual method is to use either the values that have been set out in books of mathematical tables or a slide rule. A slide rule presents a quick way of using tables, and the way in which it is used will be considered in the next section. For the present, two abbreviated tables (page 78) are given as illustrations.

Use of Trigonometrical Tables. Examples

To find Sin 33°

$$\sin 33° = \sin (30+3)°.$$

Hence find the intersection of the 30° line and the 3° column, to find

$$\sin 33° = 0.545.$$

Similarly

$$\sin 48° = 0.743$$
$$\sin 54° = 0.809.$$

The last column helps to find the values for the sines of angles which are not whole numbers of degrees. The amount that has to be added for each increase of 10' is not constant, but is reasonably constant over a small range of angles. Since they give the average increase, these columns are called the "mean differences".

To find sin 33° 20'

$$\sin 33° \ 20' = \sin (30° + 3° + 20')$$
$$= 0.545 + 0.005$$
$$= 0.550.$$

Similarly

$$\sin 33° \ 40' = 0.545 + 0.010$$
$$= 0.555.$$

$$\sin 54° 20' = 0·809 + 0·003$$
$$= 0·812.$$
$$\sin 54° 40' = 0·809 + 0·007$$
$$= 0·816.$$

To find the tangent of an angle

The method closely follows that used with sines, but it will be noticed that for large angles the mean differences are changing so rapidly that they become unreliable.

Thus $\tan 22° 20' = 0·384 + 0·007$
$$= 0·391.$$

$$\tan 55° 40' = 1·43 + 0·04$$
$$= 1·47.$$

$\tan 75° 30' =$ somewhere between 3·73 and
4·01.

Worked Examples

The shadow of a man 1·8 m tall is 3 m long. Find the elevation of the sun.

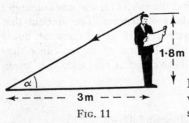

FIG. 11

From Fig. 11 we see

$$\tan \alpha = \frac{1·8}{3}$$
$$= 0·6.$$

By looking up the tables we find that α must be slightly less than 31°.

At what angle to a vertical wall must a ladder 5 m long be inclined if its base is to be 1 m from the base of the wall?

This is represented in Fig. 12. Then

$$\sin \beta = \tfrac{1}{5}$$
$$= 0·2.$$

Thus β lies between 11° and 12°, the best result being
$$\beta = 11° \, 30'. \quad (\sin 11° \, 30' = 0.199.)$$

*If a man uses the ladder set up as in the previous problem, how
far above the ground is he when he has climbed 3 m along the
ladder?*

$$\text{Angle } \alpha = (90 - 11° \, 30')$$
$$= 78° \, 30'.$$

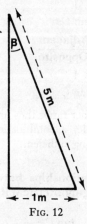

Fig. 12

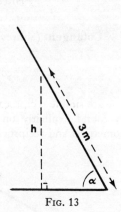

Fig. 13

From Fig. 13

$$\frac{h}{3} = \sin \alpha = \sin 78° \, 30'$$
$$\therefore h = 3 \times \sin 78° \, 30'$$
$$= 3 \times 0.98$$
$$= 2.94 \text{ m.}$$

N.B. Had we had cosine tables available, we could have made
use of the fact that $\dfrac{h}{3} = \cos 11° \, 30'$.

Other Trigonometrical Ratios

Three more ratios may be defined with reference to the
right-angled triangle (see Fig. 10):

Secant (abbrev. = sec) $= \dfrac{\text{Hypotenuse}}{\text{Adjacent}}$

$$\sec C = \frac{b}{a} = \frac{1}{\cos C}$$

Cosecant (abbrev. = cosec) $= \dfrac{\text{Hypotenuse}}{\text{Opposite}}$

$$\operatorname{cosec} C = \frac{b}{c} = \frac{1}{\sin C}$$

Cotangent (abbrev. = cot) $= \dfrac{\text{Adjacent}}{\text{Opposite}}$

$$\cot C = \frac{a}{c} = \frac{1}{\tan C}$$

As these are simple reciprocals of the other ratios they are not usually found explicitly on a slide rule, a combination of trigonometrical and reciprocal scales being sufficient.

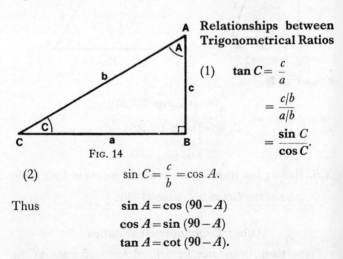

Relationships between Trigonometrical Ratios

(1) $\tan C = \dfrac{c}{a}$

$= \dfrac{c/b}{a/b}$

$= \dfrac{\sin C}{\cos C}.$

Fig. 14

(2) $\sin C = \dfrac{c}{b} = \cos A.$

Thus $\sin A = \cos(90 - A)$

$\cos A = \sin(90 - A)$

$\tan A = \cot(90 - A).$

These relationships are often useful in choosing the appropriate slide rule scales for calculations. It will be seen, for example, that a cosine scale is really superfluous.

(3) According to Pythagoras' Theorem in geometry,

$$b^2 = a^2 + c^2.$$

Now
$$a = b \cos C$$
$$c = b \sin C$$
$$\therefore b^2 = b^2 \sin^2 C + b^2 \cos^2 C$$

or
$$1 = \sin^2 C + \cos^2 C.$$

Also
$$\frac{1}{\cos^2 C} = \frac{\sin^2 C}{\cos^2 C} + 1$$

or

$$\sec^2 C = 1 + \tan^2 C.$$

Similarly $\mathbf{cosec^2\,C = 1 + cot^2\,C.}$

The Sine Rule

We now consider the relationships between the sides and angles of triangles which do not contain a right angle.

Referring to Fig. 15, in triangle ABD $z = c \sin B$ and in triangle ACD $z = b \sin C$.

Thus

$$c \sin B = b \sin C$$

or
$$\frac{b}{\sin B} = \frac{c}{\sin C}.$$

Similarly, by drawing a perpendicular from B to the line AC,

$$\frac{c}{\sin C} = \frac{a}{\sin A}$$

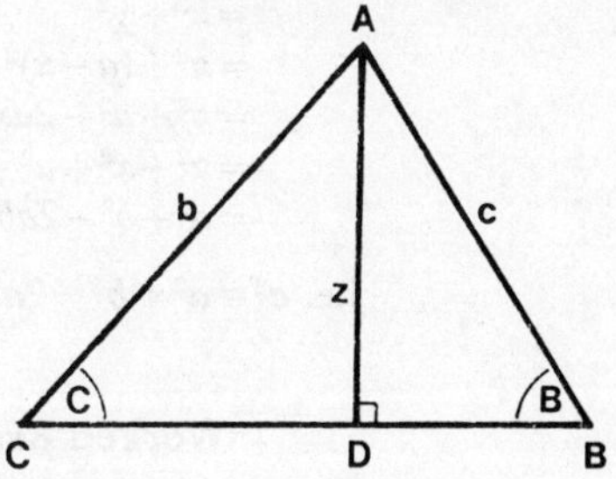

whence

$$\frac{a}{\sin A} = \frac{b}{\sin B} = \frac{c}{\sin C}.$$

Fig. 15

Worked Example

Two observers, A and B, 100 m apart, take bearings on a tree, T, relative to each other. Their readings are 65° and 55° respectively. Find the distance of the tree from A.

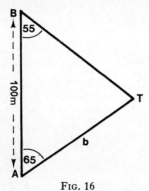

FIG. 16

The problem is represented in Fig. 16.

Angle $T = 180 - (55 + 65)$
$= 60°.$

Using the Sine Rule,

$$\frac{100}{\sin T} = \frac{b}{\sin 55}$$

$$\therefore b = \frac{\sin 55}{\sin 60} \times 100$$

$$= 99 \text{ m.}$$

The Cosine Rule

A further relationship comes from applying the theorem of Pythagoras to Fig. 15.

$$c^2 = z^2 + y^2$$
$$= z^2 + (a - x)^2$$
$$= z^2 + a^2 - 2ax + x^2$$
$$= z^2 + x^2 + a^2 - 2ab \cos C$$
$$= a^2 + b^2 - 2ab \cos C$$

i.e. $c^2 = a^2 + b^2 - 2ab \cos C.$

Worked Example

Two pieces of wood, 1·2 m and 1·5 m long, are inclined at an angle of 40°. Find the length of the piece of wood that must be nailed to their ends in order that the arrangement should be rigid.

The situation is represented in Fig. 17. Using the Cosine Rule,

$$x^2 = 1{\cdot}2^2 + 1{\cdot}5^2 - 1{\cdot}2 \times 1{\cdot}5 \times \cos 40$$
$$= 1{\cdot}44 + 2{\cdot}25 - 1{\cdot}2 \times 1{\cdot}5 \times \sin 50$$
$$= 3{\cdot}69 - 1{\cdot}38$$
$$= 2{\cdot}31$$
$$\therefore x = 1{\cdot}52 \text{ m.}$$

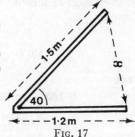

Fig. 17

Obtuse-angled Triangles

So far we have confined the sine and cosine rules to triangles with acute angles, for we do not yet have a definition for the sine of an angle which is greater than 90°. We now choose definitions which will enable us to apply the two rules to obtuse angled triangles.

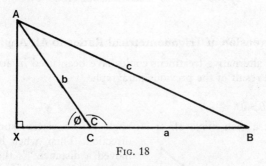

Fig. 18

In Fig. 18 AX is drawn perpendicular to BC produced. Then

$$AX = c \sin B$$
$$= b \sin \phi$$
$$\therefore \frac{b}{\sin B} = \frac{c}{\sin \phi}$$

or, if we elect to identify sin C with sin ϕ, since C is greater than 90°,

$$\frac{b}{\sin B} = \frac{c}{\sin C} \text{ as before.}$$

Rule

$$If\ 180° > \theta > 90°\ sin\ \theta = sin\ (180 - \theta).$$

Also
$$\begin{aligned}
c^2 &= AX^2 + XB^2 \\
&= AX^2 + (XC + a)^2 \\
&= AX^2 + XC^2 + 2a \cdot XC + a^2 \\
&= b^2 + 2ab \cos \theta + a^2 \\
&= a^2 + b^2 + 2ab \cos \phi
\end{aligned}$$

or
$$c^2 = a^2 + b^2 - 2ab \cos C$$
if we identify cos C with $-\cos \phi$.

Rule

$$If\ 180° > \theta > 90°\ cos\ \theta = -cos\ (180 - \theta).$$

Extension of Trigonometrical Ratios to All Angles

An alternative treatment could have been used in arriving at the result of the previous paragraph.

$90° > \theta > 0°$

Let a man move off at an angle θ to a certain specified

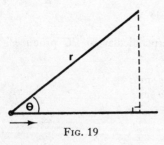

direction. Then, when he has moved a distance 'r', the distance parallel to the original direction is

$$r \cos \theta.$$

The distance moved to the left of the original line is

$$r \sin \theta.$$

FIG. 19

$180 > \theta > 90°$

When θ is between $90°$ and $180°$, distance moved parallel

$$= -r \cos \phi$$

(negative because he has moved back)

$$= r \cos \theta$$

if $\cos \theta = -\cos (180 - \theta)$.

Distance moved to left

$$= r \sin \phi$$
$$= r \sin \theta$$

if $\sin \theta = \sin (180 - \theta)$.

$$\tan \theta = \frac{\sin \theta}{\cos \theta} = \frac{\sin (180 - \theta)}{\cos (180 - \theta)} = \tan (180 - \theta).$$

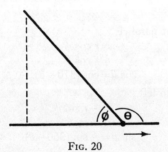

Fig. 20

$270° > \theta > 180°$

Displacement parallel

$$= -r \cos \phi$$
$$= r \cos \theta$$

if $\cos \theta = -\cos (\theta - 180)$.

Displacement to left

$$= -r \sin \phi$$

(negative because displacement is to right)

$$= r \sin \theta$$

if

$$\sin \theta = \sin (\theta - 180).$$

$$\tan \theta = \frac{\sin \theta}{\cos \theta} = \frac{-\sin (\theta - 180)}{-\cos (\theta - 180)} = \tan (\theta - 180).$$

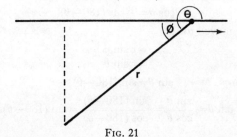

FIG. 21

$360 > \theta > 270$

Displacement parallel

$$= r \cos \phi$$
$$= r \cos \theta$$

if

$$\cos \theta = \cos (370 - \theta).$$

Displacement to left

$$= -r \sin \phi$$
$$= r \sin \theta$$

if

$$\sin \theta = -\sin (360 - \theta).$$

$$\tan \theta = \frac{\sin \theta}{\cos \theta} = \frac{-\sin (360 - \theta)}{\cos (360 - \theta)} = \tan (360 - \theta).$$

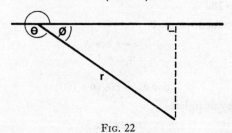

FIG. 22

All these relationships are summed up in the diagram in Fig. 23. The trigonometrical ratios which are positive in each quadrant may be remembered by the mnemonic:

All Soldiers Take   Cover

(All Sine   Tangent Cosine)

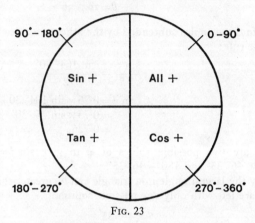

FIG. 23

Further Worked Examples

1. Three sides known

Three rods, 2 m, 1·5 m and 1 m, are connected in the form of a triangle. Find the angles between the sides.

The first step is to find the largest angle by means of the cosine rule. This angle must be opposite the largest side, so we have

$$2^2 = 1\cdot5^2 + 1^2 - 2 \times 1\cdot5 \times 1 \times \cos \theta$$

$$\therefore \frac{4 - 3\cdot25}{3} = -\cos \theta$$

$$\therefore \cos \theta = -0\cdot25.$$

The negative sign shows that θ is either between 90° and 180°, or between 180° and 270°. No angle in a triangle can be greater than 180°, so we deduce that θ is between 90° and 180°.

$$\sin 14° \, 30' = 0.25$$
$$\therefore \cos 75° \, 30' = 0.25$$
$$\therefore \cos 104° \, 30' = -0.25$$
$$\therefore \theta = \mathbf{104° \; 30'} \qquad \ldots \text{(i)}$$

To find the angles subtended by the other two sides we use the sine rule:

e.g.
$$\frac{\sin \phi}{1.5} = \frac{\sin 104° \, 30'}{2}$$

$$\therefore \sin \phi = 0.75 \times \sin 104° \, 30'$$
$$= 0.75 \times \sin 75° \, 30'$$
$$= 0.726.$$

There are two possible values of ϕ to give $\sin \phi = 0.726$, namely, 46° 35' and 180° − 46° 35'.

Only the largest angle in a triangle can be greater than 90°, so we are left with only one possible solution,

$$\phi = \mathbf{46° \; 35'} \qquad \ldots \text{(ii)}$$

The last angle can be found by making use of the fact that the angles of a triangle add up to 180°.

Thus the angle = 180° − 104° 30' − 46° 35'

$$= \mathbf{28° \; 55'} \qquad \ldots \text{(iii)}$$

2. Two sides known, and an included angle

A radar operator notes two ships, one 4 km 45° N. of E. and one 3 km 20° E. of N. Find the distance apart of the ships.

The cosine rule is again used here. The situation is represented in Fig. 24. The angle between the two bearings is

$$(90 - 45 - 0)$$
$$= 25°.$$

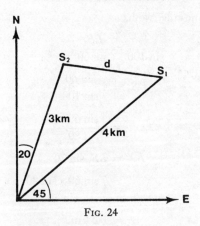

FIG. 24

Thus

$$d^2 = 3^2 + 4^2 - 2 \times 3 \times 4 \times \cos 25$$
$$= 9 + 16 - 24 \sin 65$$
$$= 25 - 21 \cdot 75$$
$$= 3 \cdot 25$$
$$\therefore \quad d = 1 \cdot 8 \text{ km}.$$

3. One side known, and all angles

The bearing of a lighthouse from a ship is $20°$ E. of N., and then, when it has steamed 4 km due North, the lighthouse has a bearing of $30°$ S. of E. How close to the lighthouse does the ship go?

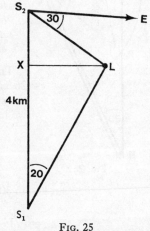

FIG. 25

This problem is illustrated in Fig. 25. The distance of closest approach is given by LX where LX is perpendicular to $S_1 S_2$.

angle $S_2 L S_1 = 100°$
angle $L S_2 S_1 = 60°$.

Using the sine rule, we have

$$\frac{4}{\sin 100} = \frac{LS_1}{\sin 60}$$

$$\therefore \ LS_1 = 4 \, \frac{\sin 60}{\sin 100}$$

$$= 4 \, \frac{\sin 60}{\sin 80}.$$

Now
$$LX = LS_1 \sin 20$$

$$= 4 \, \frac{\sin 60 \times \sin 20}{\sin 80}$$

$$= \mathbf{1 \cdot 2 \ km.}$$

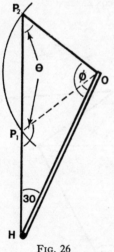

FIG. 26

4. Two sides known, and one non-included angle

One end of a rod 1 m long is hinged to a wall at H, and the other is attached to a wire 70 cm long. How high above the hinge must the wire be attached if the rod is to be inclined at an angle of 30° to the wall?

The problem is illustrated in Fig. 26 and it will be seen that two solutions are possible. Using the sine rule, we have

$$\frac{70}{\sin 30} = \frac{100}{\sin \theta}$$

$$\therefore \ \sin \theta = \sin 30 \times \frac{100}{70}$$

$$= 0 \cdot 714$$

$$\therefore \quad \theta = 45° \; 35' \quad \text{or} \quad 180 - 45° \; 35'$$
$$= 45° \; 35' \quad \text{or} \quad 134° \; 25'$$
$$\phi = 180° - 30° - \theta$$
$$\therefore \quad \phi = \mathbf{104° \; 25'} \quad \textbf{or} \quad \mathbf{15° \; 35'.}$$

If $\phi = 104° \; 25'$,

$$\frac{HP_2}{\sin 104° \; 25'} = \frac{70}{\sin 30}$$

$$\therefore \quad HP_2 = \frac{70 \times \sin 104° \; 25'}{\sin 30}$$

$$= \frac{70 \times \sin 75° \; 35'}{\sin 30}$$

$$= \mathbf{136 \; cm.}$$

If $\phi = 15° \; 35'$,

$$\frac{HP_1}{\sin 15° \; 35'} = \frac{70}{\sin 70}$$

$$\therefore \quad HP_1 = \frac{70 \times \sin 15° \; 35'}{\sin 30}$$

$$= \mathbf{31·6 \; cm.}$$

Other Trigonometrical Relationships

A brief glance at the Sine Table on page 78 will convince the reader that $\sin (30° + 40°)$ is not the same as $\sin 30° + \sin 40°$. There are, however, relationships which can be used to simplify the trigonometrical ratios for multiple angles, and, although the proofs are too lengthy for inclusion in this chapter, some of the results are given below.

$$\sin (A+B) = \sin A \cos B + \sin B \cos A$$
$$\cos (A+B) = \cos A \cos B - \sin A \sin B$$

From this we may deduce

$$\sin(A-B) = \sin A \cos(-B) + \sin(-B) \cos A$$
$$= \sin A \cos B - \sin B \cos A$$

and similarly

$$\cos(A-B) = \cos A \cos B + \sin A \sin B.$$

Also

$$\sin 2A = 2 \sin A \cos A$$
$$\cos 2A = \cos^2 A - \sin^2 A.$$

We may also show:

$$\sin A + \sin B = 2 \sin \frac{A+B}{2} \cos \frac{A-B}{2}$$

$$\sin A - \sin B = 2 \sin \frac{A-B}{2} \cos \frac{A+B}{2}$$

$$\cos A + \cos B = 2 \cos \frac{A+B}{2} \cos \frac{A-B}{2}$$

$$\cos A - \cos B = -2 \sin \frac{A+B}{2} \sin \frac{A-B}{2}.$$

Vectors

So far the trigonometrical examples have been entirely concerned with what might be broadly described as surveying. The relationships are applicable, however, whenever we have problems concerned with direction.

A vector is a quantity that has both magnitude and direction. A force pulls in a particular direction, and is therefore a vector. Velocity is a vector because, at any instant, it is associated with a particular direction.

Volume, on the other hand, has no direction associated with it. It is an example of a *scalar (a quantity which has magnitude only)*.

Resolution of Vectors

The first example, on page 76, referred to a man walking. Suppose, in fact, that he was walking at 200 m/min in a direction 30° N. of E. After 1 minute he would have moved 100 m due N. and 173 m due E. His velocity could be thought of as being composed of two velocities simultaneously, namely 100 m/min due N. and 173 m/min. due E.

More generally a velocity of V m/s at any angle $\theta°$ N, of E. can be thought of as

$$V \sin \theta \text{ due N.}$$

and $\qquad V \cos \theta$ due E.

acting simultaneously. In such a case we say we have **resolved** V into velocities parallel to and perpendicular to the northerly direction. The two values are called the **resolved components.** The same treatment can be applied to any vector.

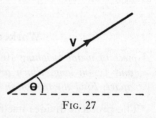

FIG. 27

Worked Example

A man pulls the rope of a sledge with a force of 200 N in a direction which is 40° to the horizontal. How much of the pull is dragging the sledge forwards?

The problem is illustrated in Fig. 28. The force of 200 N can be resolved into 200 sin 40 upwards and 200 cos 40 horizontally.

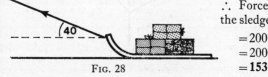

FIG. 28

∴ Force dragging the sledge forwards

$= 200 \cos 40$

$= 200 \sin 50$

$= \textbf{153 N.}$

Triangle of Vectors

The triangle of forces law, which is an example of the more general triangle of vectors, may be found stated in textbooks of mechanics as follows:

If three forces, acting at a point, are in equilibrium, they may be represented, in magnitude and direction, by the sides of a triangle. The directions must be taken in the same sense (i.e. clockwise or anticlockwise).

Many of the problems in vectors can be solved using scale diagrams, but the use of trigonometry enables greater accuracy to be achieved at greater speed. There are many possible examples and one is given below.

Worked Example

A piece of metal weighing 10 kg wt is supported by strings 1 m and 1·5 m long, which are suspended from the ceiling 2 m apart. Find the tension in the strings.

The problem divides itself into two parts:

(1) Determination of the direction of the strings

This is represented in Fig. 29a and the problem is identical to that solved on pages 89-90.

$$\therefore \quad \theta = 104° \ 30'$$
$$\phi = 46° \ 35'.$$

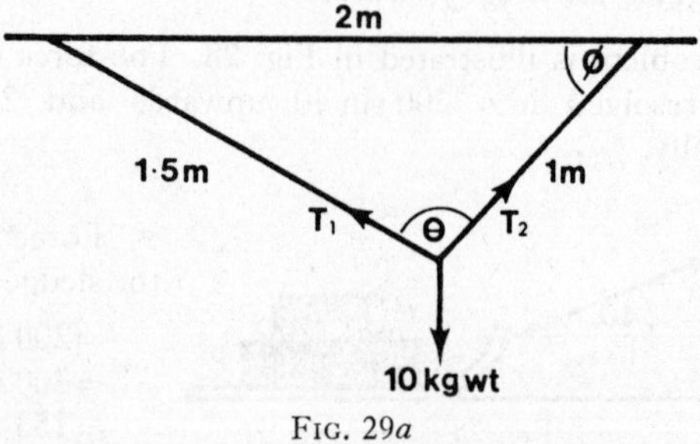

FIG. 29a

(2) Determination of the tensions

The triangle of force is shown in Fig. 29b, all forces being in a clockwise direction.

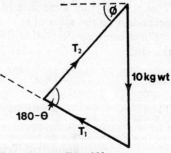

FIG. 29b

The angle opposite $T_1 = 43° 25'$.

Using the Sine Rule:

$$\frac{T_1}{\sin 43° 25'} = \frac{10}{\sin (180 - 104° 30')}$$

$$\therefore T_1 = \frac{10 \times \sin 43° 25'}{\sin 75° 30'}$$

$$= 7 \cdot 1 \text{ kg wt.}$$

Similarly

$$T_2 = \frac{10 \times \sin (90 - 28° 55')}{\sin 75° 30'}$$

$$= 9 \cdot 0 \text{ kg wt.}$$

Radians

The best known method of measuring angles is with a protractor, which divides a full revolution into 360 equal

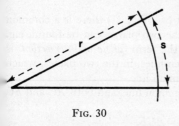

FIG. 30

degrees. An alternative (Fig. 30) is to describe an arc of radius, r, and to measure the length, s, of the arc subtended by the angle concerned. Then the value of the angle, measured in radians

$$= \frac{s}{r}.$$

This ratio is truly a measure of the angle, and is in no way dependent on the value of r.

For a complete revolution the arc is the circumference of the circle, $= 2\pi r$

$$\therefore \text{ Angle } = \frac{2\pi r}{r} = 2\pi \text{ radians.}$$

Thus π **radians** $= 180°$.

Spherical Trigonometry

Although the trigonometry of planar triangles is sufficient for small distances on the earth's surface, a word of warning is here sounded about extending the rules to large distances, for we are then dealing with spherical triangles because of the curvature of the earth.

A proof of the Sine and Cosine Rules which are applicable to spherical triangles is beyond the scope of this book, but before the results are quoted it is worth noting some important points relevant to spherical triangles.

Intersections in Three-dimensional Geometry

Line intersections

When two lines intersect there is a common point between them and an unambiguous angle.

Intersection of planes

When two planes intersect (see Fig. 31) there is a common line. Many angles between the two planes can be found, e.g. angles ACE and BCF, but the term '*angle of intersection*' is reserved for the angle between lines, in the two planes, which are perpendicular to the common line.

In the figure, CD is the common line, and both AC and EC are perpendicular to it.

Thus angle of intersection $= ACE$.

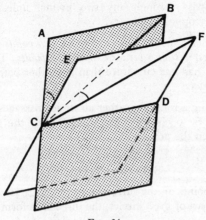

FIG. 31

Intersection of plane and sphere

Here we get a common circle (Fig. 32), and if the plane passes through the centre of the sphere we get the largest possible circle, which has a radius equal to that of the sphere. Such a circle round the sphere is called a *great circle*. An infinite number of great circles exists, but only one great

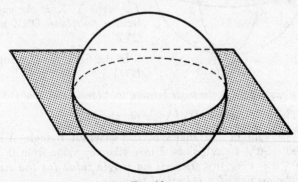

FIG. 32

circle can pass through any two points, unless they are diametrically opposite.

The line along the great circle through two points on a sphere is the shortest distance between those two points. The path is curved, but has less curvature than any other path along the sphere's surface.

In choosing a route for either air or sea passages it is usual for navigators to choose those which follow the great circle lines between the points.

Spherical Triangles

If three points on the surface of a sphere are joined by lines which are part of great circles, the three lines form a spherical triangle.

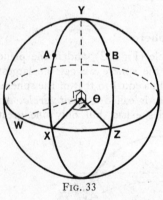

FIG. 33

In Fig. 33 three points are shown as X, Y, and Z. O is the centre of the sphere.

The angle XYZ is the angle between the planes OXY and OYZ

In the fig. it is shown as θ.

The angle YZX is the angle between the planes OXZ and OYZ

In the fig. it is 90°. (Angle *WOY*.)

The angle YXZ is the angle between the planes OXY *and* OXZ.

This angle is also 90°. (Angle not shown.)

The sum of the angles of the spherical triangle XYZ = 90° + 90° + θ, and, since θ may take any value from 0° to 180°, it is clear that *there is no single value for the sum of the angles of a spherical triangle.*

The sides of a spherical triangle are represented by the angles they subtend at the centre, rather than by the actual numerical length.

Thus, in the diagram, the side XZ is represented by angle θ. It is unusual for the side to have the same value as the angle opposite it (as is here the case). Had the triangle considered been YAB, angle AYB would still have been θ, but AB would have been represented by angle AOB, which is smaller than θ.

This method of representing distances along a great circle by the angles they subtend at the centre of the sphere is much used in navigation.

A nautical mile is the length of an arc on the earth's surface which subtends an angle of 1′ at the centre. Its value is 1852 m.

N.B. $\quad 1' = \dfrac{\pi}{180 \times 60}$ radians

$\qquad = \dfrac{1852}{R}$ radians, where $R =$ radius of the earth.

$\therefore R = \dfrac{1852 \times 180 \times 60}{\pi} = 6{\cdot}37 \times 10^6$ m.

Formulae for Spherical Triangles

Referring to Fig. 34 we have:

Cosine Rule for Spherical Triangles

$$\cos a = \cos b \cos c + \sin b \sin c \cos A$$

Sine Rule for Spherical Triangles

$$\frac{\sin a}{\sin A} = \frac{\sin b}{\sin B} = \frac{\sin c}{\sin C}$$

Worked Example

The position of New York is 40° 40′ N., 73° 50′ W., and the position of Moscow is 55° 45′ N., 37° 42′ E. If the radius of the earth can be taken as 6400 km, find the distance from New York to Moscow.

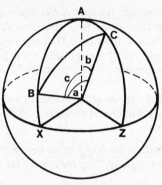

FIG. 34

Referring to Fig. 34, we may take **B** and **C** to represent New York and Moscow.

Angle $XOB = 40° \ 40'$ ∴ Angle $c = 49° \ 20'$
Angle $ZOC = 55° \ 45'$ ∴ Angle $b = 34° \ 25'$.

New York and Moscow are on opposite sides of the Greenwich Meridian,

∴ Angle $A \ (=XOZ) = 73° \ 50' + 37° \ 42' = 111° \ 32'$.

Using the Cosine Rule for Spherical Triangles

$$\cos a = \cos 34° \ 15' \cos 49° \ 20' + \sin 34° \ 15' \sin 49° \ 20' \\ \cos 111° \ 32'$$

$$= \sin 55° \ 45' \sin 40° \ 40' = -\sin 34° \ 15' \\ \sin 49° \ 20' \sin 21° \ 32'$$

$$= 0 \cdot 539 - 0 \cdot 157$$

$$= 0 \cdot 382.$$

$$\cos a = \sin (90° - a)$$

$$= 0 \cdot 382$$

$\therefore\ 90° - a = 22°\ 30'$

$\quad \therefore\ a = 67°\ 30'$

$\quad\quad = 67·5 \times \dfrac{\pi}{180}$ radians

$\quad\quad = \dfrac{BC}{6400}$

$\therefore\ BC = 67·5 \times \dfrac{\pi}{180} \times 6400$

$\quad\quad = \mathbf{7500\ km.}$

SECTION EIGHT

TRIGONOMETRICAL SCALES

SCALES are provided on many slide rules for dealing with trigonometrical work.

The slide rule so equipped can be used to provide, at an accuracy sufficient for most practical purposes, the values of sines and tangents of an angle that would otherwise require

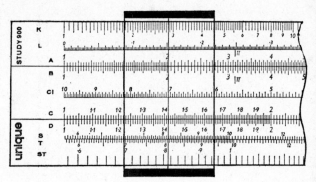

FIG. 35

a set of tables; in addition, calculations involving these functions are possible.

Trigonometrical functions have come into increasing importance with the growth of the technological society. They can be used to describe actions of a periodic nature. The wave motion theory of oscillatory waves found in radio and T.V. sound, light and vibrations analysis are everyday examples where they are used to investigate phenomena.

The previous chapter in this book is entitled "Basic Trigonometry" and it is suggested that the reader who i

104

unfamiliar with trigonometrical functions re-read this chapter before proceeding further.

A number of different scale arrangements are used on slide rules for trigonometrical work, but the Unique Study 900, which is illustrated below, shows the arrangement that has become the most popular. An examination of the illustration will show that there are three scales for trigonometrical work, and these are designated S, T and STR.

If you again examine the illustration you will find that the angles are divided into decimal parts of an angle and you will have to determine the value of the parts, i.e. between 6° and 7° on the sine scale there are 20 parts; each part therefore repre-

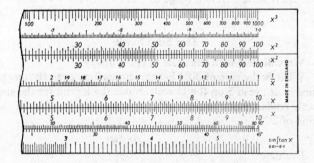

sents 0·05°. Between 25° and 30° there are 25 parts, so each part represents 0·2°. At the end of the scale the last division before 90° is 85°. You may find some slide rules where the scale is divided into minutes, i.e. between 6° and 7° there would be primary divisions for every 5 minutes (60 minutes = 1°).

The S and STR scales are really one continuous scale covering the length of the C scale twice. The STR scale is used for finding sines, tangents and radian equivalents (we will deal with radian equivalents later in this chapter). A combined scale is possible for values of sines and tangents below 6° as the differences are very small. At 4° the sine is 0·0698 and the tangent 0·0699 correct to four places of decimals; this difference is much too small to be read on a slide rule. All trigonometrical scale readings refer to the D scale (or the C scale where the trigonometrical scales are on the slide).

Small figures (called the legend) will often be found at the right hand end of each scale, these represent the range of values associated with the scale. For example; the tangent scale legend is 0·1-1 and the left-hand reading under the left-hand index of the D scale is 5·71°, the tangent for which is 0·1; whereas the right-hand reading under the right-hand index (10) on the D scale is 45°, and the tangent for 45° is 1. Similarly, the STR scale covers a range of values between 0·01 and 0·1.

The Sine Scale

We will deal with the scale of sines first.

What is the sine of 30°? Set the cursor line over 30° on the sine scale; read 5 on the D scale. Since the legend for the sine scale reads 0·1-1, the value of the answer is 0·5, which is the sine of 30°.

		Answer
Evaluate	23·5°	(0·398)
	50·25°	(0·769)
	8·05°	(0·140)

Using the STR scale evaluate

2·3°	(0·040)
5·0°	(0·087)

Things to remember

$$\text{sine } A = \cos (90° - A)$$
$$\cos A = \sin (90° - A)$$

When the cursor is set to an angle A on Scale S, it is set to sin A and to cosine (cos) $(90° - A)$ on scale C; i.e. set cursor to 30°

on S; under cursor line read 0·5 on C scale 0·5 = sin 30° = cos 60°.

Note: To find the cosines of angles greater than 84·5° use the SRT scale.

Example: Find cosine of 87°.
Write 90° − 87° = sine 3°; opposite 3° on the STR scale read on C scale 0·052 = sin 3° = cos 87°.

Note: When using the S and SRT scales, if the cursor is set to an angle on the sine scale it is also set to the sine of the angle on the C scale; it therefore follows that sines and cosines can be used in combined calculations just as square roots and reciprocals are.

To calculate 2 sin 20°:

Over 20° on the S scale set left-hand index of C scale. Under 2 on C scale read 0·648 on D. To verify your answer remember the legend for the S scale gives a range of values from 0·1 to 1·0. The sine for 20°, as read by setting the cursor line over 20° and reading the D scale, is 0·342. 0·342 × 2 = 0·648.

Problems of the type

$$\text{sine } \frac{40°}{160} = \frac{\text{sine A}}{200} \text{ can also be calculated.}$$

Answer: Over 40° on S, set 160 on C
under 200 on C read 53·48° on S.

The Tangent Scale

The Tangent Scale starts at 5·71° and goes to 45°, the value of the scale reading being between 0·1 and 1.

Values between 45° and 84·29° can also be read directly on rules having this second series of numbers engraved (usually in red) or by subtracting the angle desired from 90° and setting the resultant on the T scale.

Tan $50° = 90° - 50° = 40°$; set cursor line to T $40°$; read answer on the *CI scale*; the range of values are between 10 and 1 (remember the CI scale is a reciprocal scale and reads from right to left).

Returning to our example. With the slide rule closed over $40°$ on T, read $1 \cdot 192$ on CI scale.

Answer: Tangent of $50° = 1 \cdot 192$.

Evaluate Tan $75 \cdot 95°$

Answer: $90° - 75 \cdot 95° = 14 \cdot 05°$.

Cursor to T $14 \cdot 05$; under cursor line read $3 \cdot 995$ on CI scale.

Tan $75 \cdot 95° = 3 \cdot 995$.

Note: You may not be able to estimate the last figure very accurately, but the error between readings of $3 \cdot 990$ and $4 \cdot 0008$ is only a total of 2 minutes.

Radian Equivalents on the Small Angle Trigonometrical Scale

As mentioned earlier, the trigonometrical scale which covers from $0 \cdot 573°$ to $5 \cdot 73°$ approximately can be used for reading radians. Some scales are labelled ST for sines and tangents, and some SRT for sine, radius and tangents. It does not matter how a scale covering the above range is designated; it allows the reading of radian equivalents within its range directly, or the range can be extended by multiplying both members of the equation.

The radian is an angular measurement unit frequently used in trigonometry and higher mathematics; it is the angle subtended at the centre of a circle by an arc of radial length $\dfrac{(180°)}{\pi}$ or $57 \cdot 3°$ and that is accurate to three figures.

The radian is particularly convenient for angular velocity calculations:

$$\text{angular velocity in m/s expressed in radians/s} = \frac{\text{velocity of a point on the periphery in m/s}}{\text{radius in m}}$$

$$\text{i.e. if velocity is 30 m/s and radius is 3 m, angular velocity} = \frac{30 \text{ m/s}}{3 \text{ m}} = 10 \text{ radians/s.}$$

The simple relationship between angular velocity, linear velocity and the diameter of a revolving wheel is a powerful reason to use the radian as a unit for angular measurement.

When the cursor is set to an angle in degrees on the SRT scale, it is set to the same angle in radians on the D scale (or the C scales with the rule closed), *provided* that the D scale reading is prefixed by "0·0" as shown by the legend at the end of the scale on most slide rules.

> **Example:** Over 2° on SRT read 349 approximately; in accordance with the above rule this equals 0·0349 radians, which is correct to well within the normal slide rule accuracy.
>
> As mentioned above, multiplying both members of the equation 2°=0·0349 radian by any integer[K] positive or negative we get

$$10^K (2°) = 10^K \, 0·00349 \text{ radian}$$

i.e. (10) (2°) = 10 (0·0349) or 20° = 0·349

100 (2°) = 100 (0·0349) or 200° = 3·49 radians

1/10 (2°) = 1/10 (0·0349) or 0·2° = 0·00349 radian.

Note:

The Radian equivalent for 2° is 0·034906.

„ Sine „ „ „ „ 0·034899.

„ Tangent „ „ „ „ 0·034921.

For angles of less than 0·1 radian (5·73°) we can say that: The sine of an angle is always less than the radian equivalent and the tangent is always slightly more than the radian equivalent, but the differences are very small.

Using the method in reverse. With the cursor line on C125 read 0·716 on SRT and conclude that 0·0125 radians = 0·716°. Multiplying as before we get

(1) 0·0125 radians =   10 (0·716°)
$$= \quad 0·125 \text{ radians} = 7·16°$$

(100) 0·0125 radians = 100 (0·716°)
$$= \quad 1·25 \text{ radians} = 71·6°$$

(1/10) 0·0125 radians = 1/10 (0·716°)
$$= 0·00125 \text{ radians} = 0·0716°.$$

The Pythagoras Scale

A powerful addition to the range of trigonometrical scales found on a number of British and Continental slide rules but strangely enough omitted as far as the writer knows on

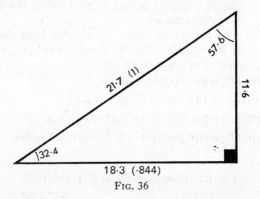

Fig. 36

American-made rules is the Pythagoras scale. Illustrated in Section 11 (the Darmstadt and Reitz Rule) is one side of the Unique Darmstadt slide rule showing a Pythagoras scale. It is designated Py or sometimes just P and it is a scale of the $\sqrt{1-x^2}$, the range of values being from 0·995 to 0. With its aid, time is saved in solving right-angled triangles, and there are many examples in technical problems and in dealing with vector quantities when it can be used with advantage.

As a matter of interest, let us time ourselves in solving a simple problem in the usual way and by using the slide rule equipped with the Pythagoras scale. We will call this scale Py for ease of expression.

Example: In a right-angled triangle the hypotenuse is 21·7 long and one other side is 18·3 long. We desire to find the remaining side and angles. (See Fig. 36.)

Square 21·7 using C and D scales = 470

„   18·3   „   „   „   = 335

Subtract   135

Extract sq. root of 135 = 11·6.

$$\tan x = \frac{11·6}{18·3} = ·633.$$

$$x = 32·4°, \quad y = 90 - 32·4° = 57·6°.$$

Results: Side   = 11·6

Angles = 32·4° and 57·6°.

If the reader will work through this first method, writing down only the necessary figures, he will probably require about 2 minutes. We used scales C and D in squaring and extracting sq. roots for the sake of accuracy. A little time could perhaps be saved by using scales A and D, but the employment of the 125 mm scales would be a disadvantage.

Solutions using the Py scale:

Divide 18·3 by 21·7 using C and D,
  which gives ·844.

Move X to 844 in Py.

Set 10C to X.

Under 217C read 1165D.

Under X read 32·4° in S.

Other angle $90 - 32·4 = 57·6°$.

Time taken, under 1 minute.

The Py scale can also be used to find the cosine of an angle from the sine without the use of complementary angles

$$\sin^2 A + \cos^2 A = 1.$$

> **Example:** Read sine of 30° using the sine scale answer on D scale 0·5, set 0·5 on Py scale and using cursor read cosine on D scale. **Answer:** 0·866. The cosine of $30° = 0·866$.

Other Trigonometrical Scales

Some earlier slide rules used a single trigonometrical scale with sines extending from 0·573° to 90° and tangents from 0·573 to 45°. This was achieved by reading against the A scale instead of the D scale. The A scale being in effect two 125 mm scales placed end to end. Although convenient, this type of scale obviously has reduced accuracy and the use of full-length scales has become almost standard practice. The devising of scales for special purposes and/or alternative ways of making calculations has, over the history of the slide rule, occupied many minds. Trigonometrical scales are a fertile field for work of this type, but many "special" scales have gained little general acceptance.

THE ELECTRICAL RULE

THE rule illustrated in Fig. 37 is designed for general purposes, but has some special features particularly related to
electrical calculations.

The two scales of temperature, Fahrenheit on the upper part
of the stock and Centigrade on the lower part, give a ready
means of converting from either thermometric scale to the
other by projection, and in addition they are designed so that
the variation in resistance of copper conductors due to change
of temperature may be determined quickly. (These two scales
lie in the part of the rule cut out in Fig. 37.)

> **Example:** A copper wire has a resistance of 2·8 ohms at
> 20°C. Find its resistance at 5°C and 200°F.
>
> Set X to 20° C. 28C to X. X to 5° C.
>
> Read 2·63 ohms under X in C.
>
> Set X to 200° F.
>
> Read 3·6 ohms under X in C.

Dynamo and Motor Efficiencies

In some makes of slide rules special 125 mm scales are fitted
for calculating efficiencies of dynamos and motors. In the rule
illustrated the same end is achieved with the aid of gauge
points, and the efficiencies are found in 250 mm scales. These
efficiencies are always of the order of 80% and 90%, and,
therefore, they are found in the crowded parts of the scales.
The advantage of using a 250 mm scale in place of the 125 mm
scale employed in other rules is obvious.

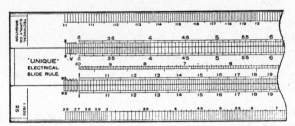

Fig. 37

Example: Calculate the efficiency of a dynamo which gives an output of 33·4 kW for 51·6 h.p.

To 334D set 516C.

Read the efficiency, 86·6%, in D opposite the gauge point N in C.

Problem 24. Calculate the efficiency of a motor which develops 161 h.p. for 137 kW.

(To h.p. in D set kW in C. Read efficiency in D or W/DF opposite gauge point W in C or CF.)

Duplicate C and D Scales

The illustration shows that the A and B scales, which we pointed out earlier as being of little value, have been omitted, and in their place 250 mm scales identical in dividing and numbering with the C and D scales are substituted. These two scales are designated by CF and DF, and they are so positioned on the rule that π in DF is immediately over 1 and 10 in D. This principle of displacing one scale relative to a similar one has been explained in Section 8. In the rule now under review all values in D are multiplied by π, by the simple process of projecting by means of the cursor from D to DF and, conversely, values in DF are divided by π when projected across to D.

There is a great number of practical problems in which π

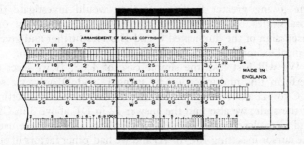

appears. Calculations relating to areas of circles, volumes and surfaces of spheres and cylinders, etc., necessitate the inclusion of π, and this arrangement of scales facilitates the manipulative operations of the rule ($\pi = 3\cdot14$).

> **Example:** Calculate the area of millboard required to make a cylindrical tube 55 mm diameter, 400 mm long.
>
> Set 1C to 55D. X to 4C.
>
> Read in CF under X.
>
> Result: 69·08 mm².

We have seen that when using the C and D scales of a standard slide rule the result is sometimes off the scale and it becomes necessary to re-set the slide by traversing it through its own length. This need never happen with the duplicated scales, since if the result is off D scale it will be found on the DF scale.

Another valuable characteristic of this rule is the additional facility it gives for setting quickly the slide and cursor, which need never be moved more than half the length of the rule for any operation.

If we remember that multiplication is effected by using the scales to add together the logarithms of the factors, the manipulation of the rule will quickly be appreciated. We are confident that many people who for years have used a slide rule equipped with the A, B, C and D scales would discard it for one giving greater facilities, if they would investigate the possibilities of other types. We will, therefore, carry our discussion of the duplicated C and D scales further and give a typical example of combined multiplication and division.

We will first take the simple case of 4×3. If we elect to perform this multiplication by using C and D only, we set 10C to 4D and read 12 in D under 3C. With the same setting of the slide, we also find the answer 12 in DF above 3 in CF, and very close to the 4 we commenced with. Now if we used the cursor in setting 10C to 4D and we had other factors in our multiplication, we should need only to move the cursor about a quarter of an inch to pick up the 3 in CF, whereas we must move it several inches if we work on the C and D scales only.

This simple exercise illustrates the saving in movement of slide and cursor when the two portions of the scales are used. We can go a step further and show how even shorter movements of the slide and cursor are possible, but this involves a complication which we prefer to avoid at this juncture. We refer to it again at a later stage.

If the reader will work through, step by step, the example following this paragraph, he will find no difficulty in using these duplicated scales, and, provided he has had some previous experience of slide rules, we predict that he will prefer this type of rule to the more usual form.

Example: Evaluate $\dfrac{4 \times 8 \times 6 \times 9}{3 \times 2 \times 16}$.

To 4D set 3C.

Set X to 8CF. 2CF to X. X to 6C. 16CF to X. X to 9CF.

Result: 18 in D under X.

It is unimportant whether the first factor is selected in D or DF, but we prefer to work as much as possible near the middle part of the rule; we choose our scales accordingly and adopt the following methods:

First method: Having selected the first factor in D or DF, and marked its position with the cursor, we move the slide to bring the second factor under X. The second factor lies in C and CF, and we take the one nearest to the cursor. We next move the cursor to the third factor *in the same C or CF scale in which the second factor was selected.* If we proceed in this manner of always taking the factors in pairs and in the same C or CF scale, the result will lie in the scale in which we selected the first factor.

Second method: There is an alternative procedure which may be adopted. We may start with the first factor in D or DF, and bring into coincidence with it the second factor *in the adjacent C or CF scale.* We then move the cursor to the third factor in C or CF, selecting that which necessitates the least movement of cursor. The intermediate result will lie in the D or DF scale, which is adjacent to C or CF scale in which the third factor was selected.

These instructions sound difficult, and in fact it is not easy to express them in words, but there is nothing complex to learn. The best way is to work through a few easy examples, and we think the reader will then agree that the duplicated C and D scales allow for more rapid working, and lead to greater accuracy.

The two methods of working we have defined may be used in conjunction with one another. We have adopted this procedure in the worked example above; the reader will see that we used the second method when using the factors 3 and 8, the second method for factors 2 and 6, and the first method for factors 16 and 9.

The reader will soon discover what appears to be a difficulty. Let us revert to the multiplication of 4×3. Set X to 4D. 1CF to X. Result is 12 in D under CF. Close to the 4 in D lies 3 in C, but if we project 3C across the slide to DF we notice the answer is apparently in error, the cursor line falling a little below 12DF. We also find in a similar manner the 2C falls below 8DF, and 5C below 20DF. In fact, all the values in C

when projected into DF give readings slightly below four times
the values in the C scale. These discrepancies are not errors
in the rule, but arise as a result of the manner in which the
scales are placed relative to one another.

If the cursor has two hair lines drawn on it, at a distance of
1·47 mm apart, the apparent departures we have observed may
be allowed for. Returning to our simple 4 × 3 example, we first
set the cursor X to 4D then brought the 1CF to X. If we now
place the left-hand cursor line over 3C, the right-hand line will
give the correct result 12, in DF. We must, therefore, bear in
mind that, in any operation in which we cross the slide to select
our second factor and re-cross to select the third factor, we
must cross the slide again, using the double line when reading
the result. We do not recommend the use of the double-line
cursor as it is liable to lead to errors, especially when we are
involved in a series of operations. If the multiple-line cursor
is used, it is advisable to use one which has a staggered line
quite separate from the central index line. The latter can be
used in the normal way, and the former for the special purpose.

At the end of this section we make a brief mention of the
type of slide rule with duplicated C and D scales which does
not require a double-line cursor for the operations we have
just discussed.

Reciprocal Scale

This scale lies along the middle of the slide, and inspection
of it discloses that it is divided in the same way as the C and
D scales, but it is reversed and reads backwards, from right to
left. We will designate this scale by CI, as in the commercial
rule.

By projecting direct from C to CI, or *vice versa*, we obtain
reciprocals—the reciprocal of any number being the result
obtained by dividing 1 by the number, e.g. the reciprocal of
is one-fifth or ·2.

Square roots are conveniently obtained with the aid of this
scale. We set the 1 or 10 of C to the number whose square root

is required in D, and then slide the cursor along until we find a position in which the readings under the cursor index in scales CI and D are identical. These readings are the square root of the number.

If the original number lies between 1 and 10, we shall set 1C to it; if between 10 and 100, we use the 10C index. For any number outside the 1—100 range we shift the decimal point in steps of two places to bring the number between 1 and 100, and after finding the square root move the decimal point in the opposite direction one place for each step of two places originally made. This procedure is more fully described in Section 5.

There is another way of determining which index of scale C should be used, or when scales A and D are being employed which half of scale A should be selected.

The rule is: If the original number has an odd number of digits preceding its decimal point or, when less than unity, has an odd number of ciphers immediately following its decimal point, the left-hand half of scale A must be used, or, if the reciprocal scale is being employed, 10C should be set to the number in D. When the number of digits preceding, or the ciphers immediately following, the decimal point in the original number is even, the right-hand half of scale A or the 1 of C must be used.

We mention this method of extracting square roots only as a matter of interest. We do not recommend it in practice. It is always better to use A and D scales, or, if these are not available, the log-log scale or the method explained in Section 4 using C and D.

In conjunction, the C, D and CI scales give a means of multiplying together three factors at one setting of the slide. Some of the standard rules, i.e. those supplied with A, B, C and D scales, are equipped with a reciprocal scale, and the property of multiplying three factors at one setting is usually claimed for this type of rule. We will investigate this feature.

Multiplication of three factors is effected by: setting the cursor to one factor in D; moving the slide to bring the second factor in CI to X; reading the result in D (or d) opposite the third factor in C (or c).

Take the simple example of $4 \times 5 \times 6$, the result of which, as we can see without using the rule, is 120.

Set X to 4D. 5CI to X. The result, under 6C in this example, is off the D scale, but if we are using a rule with CF and DF scales we find the answer, 120, in DF opposite 6CF. If, in addition to the CI scale, we have only the C and D scales available, it is necessary to traverse the slide after the first setting in order to obtain a reading, and there is no advantage in adopting this method. In a rule equipped with duplicate C and D scales, the result will always be obtainable at one setting of the slide, but occasionally it will be necessary to select the first factor in the DF scale, and when this procedure is followed the third factor must be projected across the slide to obtain the final reading on the opposite side of the stock (in DF).

Dividing by two factors with a single setting of the slide, e.g. $\dfrac{4 \cdot 26}{\cdot 035 \times 2 \cdot 88}$, can be effected with scales C, D and CI. The cursor is used to make the numerator in D (or DF). One factor of the denominator in C (or CF) is placed under X by adjusting the slide, and the result is read in D (or DF) opposite the remaining factor in R. In this type of calculation, when using the ordinary rule, we find the same limitations, the result fairly frequently being off the scale. When this occurs, a second setting becomes necessary, and again there is no saving in time over and above using the C and D scales in the usual manner. The rule with duplicated C and D scales is much more convenient, the result always being obtainable at one setting of the slide.

THE DUALISTIC RULE

In Section 9 we examined the Electrical rule, which includes as part of its scale equipment duplicated C and D scales. We attempted to show that a saving of time can be effected when this type of rule is used. We explained that the CF and DF scales are identical with the C and D scales, but that the former are positioned so that the π in CF is immediately over the 1 and 10 of C and the π in DF over the 1 and 10 of D. This arrangement of scales enables the user to multiply or divide by π merely by projecting by means of the cursor index X from D to DF or *vice versa*. We pointed out that a special 2-line cursor is necessary if full advantage is to be taken of the duplicated scales.

We propose now to study a type of rule which, although closely resembling the Electrical rule in respect of the duplicated scales, is different in some respects.

In this particular rule, shown in Fig. 38, the 1 of CF is immediately above $\sqrt{10}$ in C and, similarly, the 1 of DF is directly over $\sqrt{10}$ in D. Now $\sqrt{10}$ (which is exactly mid-way between 1 and 10 of any scale, as will be agreed if a little consideration is given to the logarithms of the numbers) has a value very near to 3·16 and thus is not far removed from $\pi(=3\cdot14)$, so at first sight the two rules we are comparing may appear identical in the layout of their duplicated C and D scales.

The slight difference in the relative positions of the "folded" scales means that we cannot with the Dualistic rule multiply or divide by π by simple projection, but, as a compensation, the 2-line cursor is not required for the comprehensive use of the Dualistic rule.

(The reader will readily appreciate that an additional broken

line can easily be added to the cursor to provide the facility of
multiplying and dividing by π, but we do not recommend such
an addition. In any event, the point is of no great importance
since the other features of the duplicated C and D scales are
predominant.)

Apart from work of a specialised nature, probably 90% of
the computations effected by slide rule involve the use of the
C and D scales only. In the Dualistic rule these scales occupy
their usual positions. They are designated by the symbols C_1

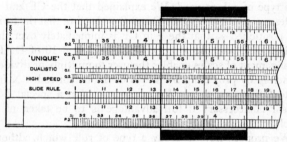

and D_1, and lie along the lower edge of the slide and on the
adjacent edge of the stock respectively, as seen in Fig. 38.

The upper margin of the slide, and the edge of the stock
adjacent to it, are equipped with modified C and D scales.
These are designated by C_2 and D_2 respectively, and are used
in conjunction with the C_1 and D_1 scales, as described below.

The extreme margins of the stock and the centre of the slide
are provided with a pair of 500 mm scales. These will be
recognised as the principal scales of the 10/20 rule. They may
be used separately; they are equivalent to a 500 mm rule and
give the same high degree of accuracy. Scale references P_1, P_2,
Q_1 and Q_2. These scales may be used in conjunction with the
C_1 and D_1 scales, as will be demonstrated presently.

On the reverse of the slide three scales, LL_1, LL_2 and LL_3,
will be found; these are three sections of a continuous log-log

scale, extending from 1·01 to 40,000, and are used with the slide inverted in conjunction with the D_1 scale.

C_1 and D_1 Scales

As stated above, these are the C and D scales of the standard type slide rule. The instruction given in Section 4, dealing with the operations of multiplication and division, apply without modification, except that C and D should be read as C_1 and D_1

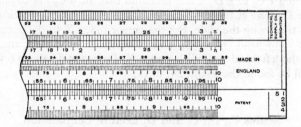

respectively. In all cases when a calculation involves the use of the C and D scales only, the standard slide rule or the Dualistic rule may be used without any discrimination.

C_2 and D_2 Scales

On inspection, it will at once be seen that these two scales are divided in the same manner as the C_1 and D_1 scales, but they are placed differently on the rule. The 1 of the scales C_2 and D_2 is in the middle of the length of the rule. The scales commence at π at the left-hand end of the rule; the readings increase, reaching 10 (or 1) at the mid-point, and then increase, reaching π at the right-hand extremity of the rule.

Scales C_2 and D_2 should not be used alone for multiplication and division. A few simple examples will at once show that, although multiplication or division may be effected with their aid, frequently the result is off the scale at the first setting and cannot be obtained without traversing the slide through its own length. The same dilemma sometimes arises with the C_1 and D_1 scales when multiplying, but the traversing of the slide is rather more easily effected. In any case, there is no advantage gained by using C_2 and D_2 in preference to C_1 and D_1, and since all slide rule users are familiar with the C_1 and D_1 scales it is advisable to adhere to them. To illustrate this point the reader is asked to compute 6×4 using C_2 and D_2 scales. On setting 1 C_2 to 4 D_2 it will be found that the 6 C_2 lies beyond the D_2 scale at the left-hand end. The result may be obtained by traversing the slide. Set the cursor index X to the π near the right-hand end of C_2, and move the slide to bring the π at the left-hand end of C_2 under X. Immediately above 6 C_2 will be found the result, 24, in D_2.

Scales C_1, D_1, C_2 and D_2 used in Conjunction

Computations involving multiplication and/or division are more rapidly effected when using these four scales than when C_1 and D_1 only are employed. The following example is designed to illustrate this feature:

Compute the value of $\dfrac{3 \cdot 1 \times 6 \cdot 4 \times 9 \cdot 2}{1 \cdot 5 \times 11 \cdot 2}$.

Using C_1 and D_1 only, and performing division and multiplication alternately since this saves time, the following operations are required:

To $31D_1$ set $15C_1$.

Set X to $1C_1$. $10C_1$ to X. X to $64C_1$. $112C_1$ to X. X to $1C_1$ $10C_1$ to X.

Result: 109 in D_1 immediately under $92C_1$.

Approximation, performed mentally, shows the answer is of the order 10, and the result is therefore 10·9.

Using the four scales:

To $31D_1$ set $15C_1$.

Set X to $64C_2$. $112C_2$ to X.

Result: 109 in D_2 above $92C_2$.

If the rule is used to carry out these two series of operations, it will be found that by using all four scales the number of movements of slide and cursor is greatly reduced and the actual distances through which the slide and cursor are moved in these various operations are very much smaller. Greater accuracy will be attained, because in the course of time all slide rules develop small errors in their scales due to shrinkage or other distortion, and scales which originally were identical differ slightly in length. Critical inspection will almost invariably show that in slide rules which have been in use for some time the overall lengths of scales on slide and stock differ slightly. With such a rule, imagine multiplication of 12×4 is being effected using C_1 and D_1 scales. Set $1C_1$ to $12D_1$ and the result, 48, appears in D_1 under $4C_1$. If the slide scale has, through shrinkage, become, say, slightly shorter than the stock scale, a small error will be seen, the $4C_1$ falling just below the $48D_1$. Using the Dualistic rule, set $1C_1$ to $12D_1$ and read the result, 48, in D_2 over $4C_2$. With this setting the length of slide scale used is only about 25 mm, and the error will be only about one-seventh of that involved in using the C_1 and D_1 scales, where the length of slide employed is about 175 mm. The same argument applies to any series of operations.

The principle involved in using the four scales of the Dualistic rule is the same as that employed in slide rules generally. Multiplication and division are effected by adding or subtracting logarithms, but with two sets of scales available there are alternative scale readings provided, and the manipulation of the rule is easier and speedier than in the case of the standard slide rule.

In using the Dualistic rule the first factor is selected in the D_1 or D_2 scales. The choice of scales is unrestricted, but it is

an advantage to start with that scale in which the first factor
lies near the middle of the length of the rule. If the first factor
lies between 2 and 6 use the D_1 scale, but if it lies between 6
and 2 start in the D_2 scale. For the factors used subsequently
there are alternative scale readings, and the one lying nearest
should be used. An example will make this selection of factors
clear.

Example: Evaluate $3 \times 1 \cdot 2 \times \frac{9}{4} \times 2 \cdot 5$.

Set $1C_2$ to $3D_1$ (using X). X to $12C_2$. $4C_1$ to X. X to
$9C_2$. $1C_2$ to X. X to $25C_1$.

Result in D_1 under X is $20 \cdot 2$.

It will at once be noticed that the movements of slide and
cursor are small compared with those necessary if the C_1 and
D_1 scales are used alone.

Whether the final result appears in D_1 or D_2 depends upon
which scales, C_1 or C_2 ,were used for the intermediate factors;
the determination presents no difficulty. Very often, especially
in short computations, the order of the result is already known,
and the slide rule is used to obtain an accurate figure. In such
cases it is only necessary to glance at the results lying in D_1
and D_2 under X. These values differ in the ratio of $\sqrt{10}$ to 1,
i.e. about $3 \cdot 16$ to 1. In such a case the appropriate reading will
be obvious.

In longer computations, when the result is not obvious, a
rough approximation should be made to determine the position
of the decimal point. This approximation will also disclose in
which of the two scales D_1 or D_2 the result lies.

The following method for determining in which scale the
result lies may be preferred, and the reader is advised to spend
a few minutes making himself familiar with it, since it also
applies to the 500 mm scales, which will be dealt with later. The
method may, at first reading, sound complicated. It is, in fact,
very easy of application and has been explained earlier in
Section 9, but we think some repetition here may be desirable

We have in mind also the fact that an experienced slide rule user may be reading this section without having perused the earlier notes.

Every multiplication or division, or combined multiplication and division, involves using two factors in the C scale. In a multiplication the 1 (or 10) C is set to some value in D, and the result found in D opposite the multiplying factor in C. In division the divisor in C is first set and the result read opposite the 1 (or 10) C, and in multiplication/division the divisor in C is set and the quotient obtained opposite another factor in C. In applying the method—which we believe to be original—it is only necessary to observe whether the two factors are both in the same C scale or whether one is in C_1 and the other in C_2. If the two factors are selected in different sections of the C scale, the result is obtained by crossing from D_1 to D_2, or *vice versa*; if both factors lie in the same part of the C scale, the result will be found in that part of the D scale in which the number being multiplied or divided appeared.

A simple example may assist. Suppose multiplication of 8×3 is desired. There are six different ways of obtaining the result, 24; they are:

(a) Set   1 C_2 to 8 D_2 Result in D_2 opposite 3 C_2

(b) ,,   1 C_2 to 8 D_2 ,,   ,, D_1 ,,   3 C_1

(c) ,,   10 C_1 to 8 D_1 ,,   ,, D_1 ,,   3 C_1

(d) ,,   10 C_1 to 8 D_1 ,,   ,, D_2 ,,   3 C_2

(e) ,,   1 C_2 to 8 D_1 ,,   ,, D_2 ,,   3 C_1

(f) ,,   10 C_1 to 8 D_2 ,,   ,, D_1 ,,   3 C_2

the cursor index X being used in setting where necessary.

In the first and third settings of the slide the two factors 1 and 3 lie in the same section of the C scale, namely, both in C_2 in the first and both in C_1 in the third method. In both, the result lies in the section of the D scale in which the factor 8 was chosen. In the other four methods the factors 1 and 3 lie in opposite sections of the C scale, and the result is always in the opposite section of the D scale from that in which the first factor 8 was selected.

In the simple example just cited it is easy to determine in which part of the D scale the result will be found, but in a longer one it is advisable to record the various operations as now suggested. When the first slide setting is made, note which section of the D scale is used and jot down D_1 or D_2 as the case may be. If in the next operation the two factors used are in the same section of the C scale, take no further notice of them, but if they are in different sections of the C scale write a stroke thus, /, following the D_1 or D_2. Proceed in this way, making a stroke each time scale C_1 and C_2 are both used in any one setting of the slide, the second stroke cancelling the first by changing it into a $\times$, so the record starting with, say, D_1 would next become $D_1/$, and then $D_1 \times$. At the end of the computation the record will finish either with D_1, or $D_1/$, or $D_1 \times$. If the last symbol is a stroke, the final result will lie in the D_2 scale; in other cases it will lie in D_1.

Example: Evaluate $\dfrac{2 \cdot 8 \times 93 \times 107 \times 46}{18 \times 52 \times 29}$.

Set X to 28D_1 and jot down D_1.

,, 18C_2 to X }
,, X to 93C_1 }   ,,   ,,   /

,, 52C_1 to X }
,, X to 107C_2 }   ,,   ,,   /

,, 29C_1 to X }
,, X to 46C_1 } No symbol necessary here.

Under X read 472 in D_1, and 1495 in D_2.

The symbols when written down in line result in $D_1 \times$; the indication is that the result is in D_1. Approximation gives 46 and the result is 47·2.

The 500 mm Scales

The scales lying along the top and bottom edges of the face of the stock, designated by the symbols P_1 and P_2 respectively, together form a 500 mm logarithmic scale and, in combination with a similar pair of scales placed in the middle of the slide and designated by Q_1 and Q_2, form the equivalent of a 500 mm slide rule.

When a higher degree of accuracy than can be derived from the 250 mm C and D scales is desired, the P and Q scales should be used. Inspection of the illustration will show the additional dividing which has been made possible by the use of these long scales.

Multiplication and division are effected by using the P and Q scales and the cursor index X. The method given earlier for determining whether the final result should be read in D_1 or D_2 may be adopted when there is any doubt as to whether the result appears in P_1 or P_2. This method has already been dealt with fully and need not be repeated. Two examples are now given to illustrate the use of the 10/20 scales.

Example: Evaluate $\dfrac{13 \cdot 65 \times 23 \cdot 4}{39 \cdot 6}$.

Set X to $1365P_1$. $396Q_2$ to X. X to $234Q_1$.

Result is 807 in P_2.

The value in P_1 under X is 255 and it is obvious that this result is incorrect. 396 appeared in Q_2 and 234 in Q_1, therefore the result must be in P_2, since the first factor, 1365, is in P_1. It is quite unnecessary to write down the symbols, but if, for illustration only, we do so, they will be $P_1/$. The stroke at the end indicates the final result is in the opposite scale to that in which the first factor, 1365, was found: 13 into 39 is 3, and 3 into 24 gives 8 as an approximate result. Now, with two values under X, 807 and 255, there is no difficulty in selecting the correct one and at the same time inserting the decimal point. Result: 8·07.

A longer example is now given:

$$\text{Evaluate } \frac{4 \cdot 4 \times 69 \cdot 2 \times 24 \cdot 6 \times 1 \cdot 246 \times 36}{15 \cdot 1 \times 82 \times 2 \times 18 \cdot 6 \times 28 \cdot 1}.$$

Set X to 44P_2. Note down P_2.

$\left.\begin{array}{l} 151Q_1 \text{ to X} \\ \text{X to } 692Q_2 \end{array}\right\}$ ”   ”   /

$\left.\begin{array}{l} 822Q_2 \text{ to X} \\ \text{X to } 246Q_1 \end{array}\right\}$ ”   ”   \\

$\left.\begin{array}{l} 186Q_1 \text{ to X} \\ \text{X to } 1246Q_1 \end{array}\right\}$ No symbol required here.

$\left.\begin{array}{l} 281Q_1 \text{ to X} \\ \text{X to } 10Q_2 \end{array}\right\}$ Note down /

$\left.\begin{array}{l} 1Q_1 \text{ to X} \\ \text{X to } 36Q_2 \end{array}\right\}$ ”   ”   \\

The symbols written in line should appear $P_2 \times \times$, showing the result is in P_2. It is 519.

Approximation: 4·4 into 15 is slightly over 3, which divides into 69 about 20: 20 into 82, say, 4, 4 into 24 gives 6, 6 into 18 is 3, and 3 into 36 gives 12; 12 times 1·2 is 14 approximately and we are left with $\frac{14}{28} = \cdot 5$ as the approximate result. The actual result is, therefore, ·519; it lies in P_2, as indicated by the symbols.

The procedure explained in Section 4 for determination of position of decimal point may be used if desired, but we strongly recommend the approximation method as being easier and safer. In a long computation there is a risk that a factor may be inadvertently omitted in the slide rule manipulation. The approximation if carefully made will disclose the error—another sound reason for making it.

The reader is now advised to practise the use of this new rule by working through a few simple examples, the results of which may easily be checked. It is confidently predicted that when familiarity with the scales is attained the rule will make an appeal as being superior to the standard type. The difficulties—if there are any—have now been dealt with and the remaining instruction deals with simple points.

Squares and Square Roots

The relative positions of the 250 mm and 500 mm scales give a ready means of evaluating squares and square roots. The square of any number is obtained by projecting by means of X the number from either Q_1 or Q_2 into C_1. For example, 1·6, when projected from Q_1 into C_1, gives 2·56. When projecting from Q_2 to C_1, the squares are 10 times the actual values of the numbers engraved along the C_1 scale. 5 in Q_2 lies immediately above 2·5 in C_1, and this value must be read as 25. Readers now familiar with the A, B, C and D scales of a standard rule will notice the similarity in procedure. They will also notice the higher degree of accuracy possible with the longer scales.

Square roots are obtained by the reverse process of projecting from C_1 into Q_1 or Q_2. Square roots of numbers from 1 to 10 are obtained by projection from C_1 into Q_1, and square roots of numbers from 10 to 100 by projection from C_1 into Q_1. When a number whose square root is desired lies outside the range 1 to 100, the procedure outlined in Section 5 should be used, reading Q_1 for the left-hand half of scale A and Q_2 for the right-hand half.

Scales P_1, P_2 and D_1 may be used for squares and square roots if preferred; the procedure will be obvious from the instructions given above.

Cubes and Cube Roots

Cubes are easily obtained by setting the 1 (or 10) of C_1 to the number in D_1; the cube lies in D_1 immediately below the number in Q_1 or Q_2. To cube 2·2 set $10C_1$ to $2·2D_1$; set X to $2·2Q_1$ and read in D_1 under X the result, 10·65, the decimal point being inserted by inspection.

Cube roots are evaluated by setting X to the number in D, and then moving the slide until the value in D_1 coincident with 1 (or 10) C_1 is the same as the number in Q_1 or Q_2 under X. Suppose the cube root of 2 is required. Set X over 2 in D_1; now move the slide about an inch to the right of its mid-position, and then carefully adjust it until the value in D_1 coincident with $1C_1$ is the same as the value in Q_1 under the cursor index X; this value will be found to be 1·26, which is the cube root of 2 (1·25992).

It may assist to observe that:

If the number lies within the range 1-10 its cube root will be found in Q_1 and coincident with $1C_1$.

If the number lies within the range 10 - 31 (π^3) its cube root will be found in Q_1 and coincident with $10C_1$.

If the number lies within the range 31-100 its cube root will be found in Q_2 and coincident with $1C_1$.

If the number lies within the range 100 - 1000 its cube root will be found in Q_2 and coincident with $10C_1$.

Numbers from 1 to 1000 have cube roots from 1 to 10. If the number whose cube root is required is not within the range 1-1000 it should first be altered by moving the decimal point three, or multiples of three, places to right or left to bring the number within that range. The cube root should then be found as detailed above, and finally the decimal point of the result should be moved *back* one place for each step of three places made in the original number.

Example: Find the cube root of 116,300.

Moving the decimal point three places to the left alters the figure to 116·3, which lies within the 1 to 1000 range. The cube root of 116·3 is 4·88. The decimal point must now be moved one place to the right, giving the actual result as 48·8.

In evaluating cube roots it is a good plan to find the nearest integral result mentally.

Example: Find the cube root of ·682. First move the decimal point three places to the right, so that the number becomes 682. The cube of 5 is 125, which is well below 682. Try the cube of 7; $7 \times 7 = 49$ (say 50); $7 \times 50 = 350$, still too small; try 9; $9 \times 9 = 81$; and $9 \times 80 = 720$. The required cube root is less than 9. Set X over $682D_1$, and the slide so that $10C_1$ is over $9D_1$. Now move the slide slowly to the left until the reading in D_1 below 10C is the same as that in Q_2 under X. These identical values are 8·8. The cube root of 682 is 8·8, and of ·682, ·88.

Squares, square roots, cube and cube roots may be evaluated easily with the aid of the log-log scales, often with a higher degree of accuracy than can be attained with the P and Q scales.

Log-log Scales

When the log-log scale is used the slide should be inverted so that the surface which generally is underneath is brought uppermost, or, if the log-log scale is fitted to a separate slide, the slides should be interchanged. The log-log scale provides a means of effecting unusual computations. *Its most useful property is the ease with which powers and roots may be evaluated, even when the power root is a mixed number.*

Suppose the value of $8·4^{1·79}$ is required. Set $8·4LL_3$ to $1D_1$, then immediately above $1·79D_1$ will be found the result, 45·1, in LL_3. If the index of the power is negative, e.g. $8·4^{-1·79}$, the value of $8·4^{1·79}$ should first be evaluated and the reciprocal of this found, using the C and D scales:

$$\text{i.e.} \quad 8·4^{-1·79} = \frac{1}{45·1} = ·0222.$$

To evaluate $^{4\cdot15}\sqrt{1\cdot31}$: to 415$D_1$ set 1·31LL_2, and then use X to project 10D_1 into LL_1 and read the result 1·067.

Results outside the range of the log-log scale may be obtained by the methods suggested in Section 6.

Logarithms to any base may be obtained by setting the base in LL to 1 of D_1, or 1 of D_2, and projecting the number whose log is required from the log-log scale into D_1 or D_2. The log so obtained will be complete, comprising characteristic and mantissa. Common logarithms are found by setting the 10LL_3 to 1D_1. It will be seen that immediately below 100LL_3 stands 2D_1, 2 being the log of 100. Below 1000 stands 3 and below 10,000 stands 4. To obtain the logs of numbers in LL_1 and LL_2 the cursor index must be used to project into D_1. If the number whose log is required lies towards the left-hand end of the log-log scale, 10LL_3 should be set to 10D_1, or 1D_2.

Natural logarithms are obtained by setting the value 2·7183 near the left-hand end of the LL_3 scale to the 1 of D_1. This setting will enable all the natural logs of numbers within the range of the log-log scale to be read without moving the slide; the numbers in LL_1 and LL_2 being projected into D_1 by using the cursor index X.

It is useful to remember that the 10th powers of numbers in LL_1 lie immediately below in LL_2, and the 10th power of numbers in LL_2 lie immediately below in LL_3.

THE DARMSTADT RULE AND THE RIETZ RULE

ALTHOUGH an almost infinite variety of scales suitable for use on a slide rule are possible, in practice (excluding scales devised for special purposes) some thirty different scales cover the range in general use.

The layout of the scales, however, even if you limit yourself to the thirty in general use, permits of a lot of variation and it is therefore not surprising that certain arrangements have become popular.

If you want to know how many scale arrangements are possible with 30 scales, this is known as factorial 30 (written 30!) the answer is obtained by multiplying each number by the next one, i.e. $1 \times 2 \times 3 \times 4 \ldots \times 29 \times 30$. You come to quite a big number.

One of the most popular arrangements both in this country and on the Continent is known as the Darmstadt. The scale arrangement is more extensive than can be reasonably accommodated on the single face of a slide rule, but to keep the cost low, on the Unique Darmstadt rule, some of the scales are placed on the reverse of the slide.

The scale equipment on the face, as shown on the illustration, is:

Scales A, B, C and D.

Reciprocal Scale CI ref. $\dfrac{1}{X}$.

Cubes and cube root scale K ref. X^3.

Logarithmic Scale L.

Sine Scale $\left.\begin{array}{l}\end{array}\right\}$ 360° system, decimally subdivided, ref.
Tangent Scale $\left.\begin{array}{l}\end{array}\right\}$ S and T.

Pythagoras Scale Py ref. $\sqrt{1-x^2}$.

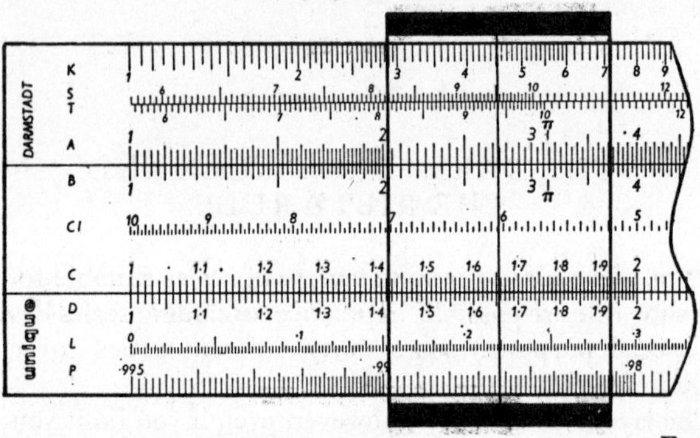

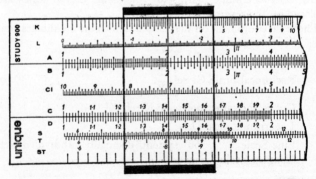

FIG. 39

On the reverse of the slide is a three-section log-log scale LL1 ref. $e^{0.01x}$, LL2 ref. $e^{0.1x}$ and LL3 ref. e^x covering together the range 1·01 to 30,000. These powerful scales will provide roots, powers and logarithms to any base, and are also invaluable for compound interest calculations.

Sine Scale

Since $\sin^2 A + \cos^2 A = 1$, it follows that the values of $\sin A$ and $\cos A$ will be found in D and Py respectively if the cursor index is set to A in the sin scale. (**Example**—set cursor to 30° and find ·5 in D and ·866 in Py.)

FIG. 40

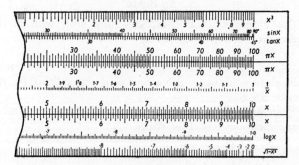

Tan Scale

Line up the slide so that scales C and D coincide. By projecting from the T scale, the tangent and cotangent appear in D and CI respectively. (**Example**—tan $13\cdot4° = \cdot238$ and cotangent $13\cdot4 = 4\cdot2$.)

K Scale

Numbers in D are cubed when projected in K. Cube roots of numbers are found by projecting from K into D.

L Scale

The mantissae of common logs of the numbers in D appear directly below in L. (**Example**—log $2 = \cdot3010$.)

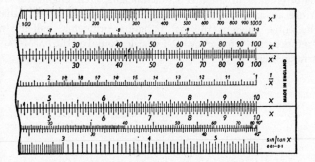

Py Scale

The Pythagoras scale has been fully dealt with in the section on trigonometrical scales.

Another standard scale arrangement is known as the RIETZ. This pattern of scale arrangements is exemplified by the Unique S.900.

As an inspection of the illustration will show the "RIETZ" arrangement consists of ten scales, viz.:

Scales A, B, ref. X^2.

Scales C, D, ref. X.

Reciprocal Scale CI ref. $\dfrac{1}{X}$.

Scale K cube and cube root, ref. X^3.

Logarithmic Scale L.

Sine Scale, ref. S.

Tangent Scale, ref. T.

Low values of angles, a combined sine and tangent scale
      that will also give the angle in radians, ref. ST.

A scale layout of this type has been found to cover the general requirements of architects, technicians, civil engineers, etc. More advanced work involving roots to higher powers than the cube, such as thermal radiation problems, half-life of Isotopes, etc., require the log-log scales found on the DARMSTADT arrangement.

THE CHEMICAL RULE

ANOTHER example of a completely special type of slide rule is the Unique Chemical Slide Rule.

This rule exemplifies the use made throughout slide rule work of the proportion principle or, as it is sometimes called, the Rule of 3. Stated simply: if $a = b$, $c = x$. Because of the rather unusual nature of the Chemical slide rule, we are giving details taken from the instructions for this rule for volumetric analysis and this will demonstrate fully the Rule of 3 principle used for work that one would not normally associate with a slide rule.

The rule also contains the International Table of Atomic Weights arranged in alphabetical order of their chemical symbols for ready reference, while on the reverse face the Periodic Table of the Elements is conveniently set out.

Volumetric Analysis

A normal solution is one which contains the gramme equivalent weight of the dissolved substance in 1 litre of solution. Usually a litre does not contain the exact equivalent weight of the dissolved substance, in which case the solution may be 0·5 N (where half the equivalent weight is dissolved), 0·25 N, 0·12 N, etc.

In the case of a primary standard the normality is calculated from the weight taken. In this case:

$$\text{Normality} = \frac{\text{weight of substance (grammes) per litre of solution}}{\text{equivalent weight of substance (grammes)}}$$

e.g. sodium carbonate has an equivalent weight of 53. If 5·3 grammes are taken and made up to a litre, the solution is

$$0 \cdot 1 \text{ N} \left(\text{or } \frac{\text{N}}{10} \right).$$

A solution of a primary standard may be made up by dissolving a definite weight of the substance in distilled water and making it up to a litre. The normality of this solution is then calculated as above.

By titration with a suitable primary standard a given solution may be standardised, that is, its normality may be determined.

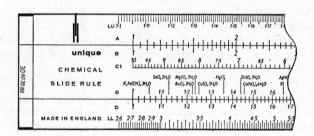

Fig. 41

This solution may then be used to determine the strength of other solutions.

If the normality of a pipette solution is denoted by Np

,,	,,	,, burette ,,	,,	,, Nb
,, volume	,, pipette ,,	,,	,, Vp
,, ,,	,, burette ,,	,,	,, Vb

then:

$$NbVb = NpVp$$

or

$$\frac{Nb}{Vp} = \frac{Np}{Vb}.$$

Calculation of normality of pipette solution using slide rule (standard solution in burette)

(1) Place pipette volume on scale B opposite normality of standard solution on scale A.

(2) Read off normality of pipette solution on scale A opposite volume of burette solution required, on scale B.

Numerical Example: It is required to find the normality of a given solution of NaOH.

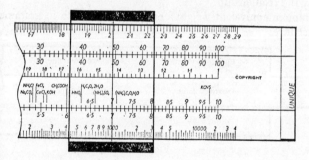

Procedure: 24 ml of the NaOH solution are placed in a conical flask and titrated with 0·12 N-HCl solution using a suitable indicator. 22·5 ml to HCl are required for neutralisation.

Calculation of result, using slide rule

Place figure 25 on scale B opposite figure 12 on scale A and read off normality of NaOH solution on scale A opposite figure 22·5 on scale B. This gives normality of NaOH solution as 0·108. It will facilitate calculations if the rule is always adjusted as shown in the sketch. If this arrangement is followed when any three quantities are known, the fourth may be readily obtained. For convenience, pipette volumes are underlined on scale B. It should be noted, however, that generally the pipette volumes will occur on the left-hand side of scale B, e.g. pipette volume 15 mm³ would be represented by figures 1·5 on scales C and D, not 15. The underlining of pipette volumes is omitted on the left-hand side of the scale to enhance its clarity.

Calculation of strength of a solution in grammes per litre, when its normality is known, by means of slide rule

The strength of a solution in grammes per litre is governed by the relationship:

gramme equivalent weight × normality = strength in grammes per litre.

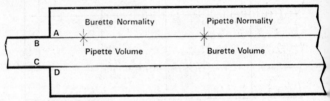

Fig. 42

(1) Place figure 1 on scale C opposite the normality of the solution on scale D.

(2) Read off strength of given solution in grammes per litre on scale D opposite the gauge point representing the gramme equivalent weight of the given substance on scale C.

Numerical Example: It is required to find the strength of a 0·108 N solution of NaOH in grammes per litre.

Procedure: Place figure 1 on scale C opposite normality of given solution (0·108) on scale D and read off strength of NaOH solution on scale D opposite gramme equivalent weight of NaOH (40·01) on scale C. This gives strength of NaOH solution as 4·32 grammes per litre.

INDICES AND LOGARITHMS

IN the foreword we said that for the benefit of those who desire to learn something of logarithms we would give a simple explanation of the nature and qualities of this intriguing chapter of mathematics. We shall not take the reader into deep waters, but shall confine our remarks to the elementary parts of the subject.

Indices

We must first learn a few simple rules concerning the raising of numbers to different powers.

We prefer to let our numbers or quantities be represented by letters, such as a, or b, or m, or n, but we shall sometimes use actual figures. The reader will have seen in technical books, or in newspapers, such expressions as a^2, b^3, m^5 or n^8, and he may have speculated as to what the small figures printed on the right-hand side above the letters signify. The numbers 2, 3, 5 and 8 are termed indices of a, b, m or n respectively. a^2 means $a \times a$, and is read as a squared; b^3 means $b \times b \times b$ and is read b cubed. Similarly for m^5, which is read m to the 5th power, or simply m to the fifth, and n to the eighth. The index of a number, therefore, indicates how many times 1 is to be multiplied by the number. The indices in the above examples are all positive integers, i.e. whole numbers. Indices may be positive $(+)$ or negative $(-)$. They may be numbers or fractions, e.g. a^2, a^{-4}, $a^{\frac{1}{2}}$, $a^{-\frac{2}{3}}$.

a^{-4} is a different way of writing $\dfrac{1}{a^4}$.

$a^{\frac{1}{2}}$,,   ,,   ,, $\sqrt{a}$.

$a^{-\frac{2}{3}}$,,   ,,   ,, $\dfrac{1}{a^{\frac{2}{3}}}$.

$a^{\frac{5}{3}} = \sqrt[3]{a^5}$, which, expressed in words, is the cube root of the fifth power of a.

There are three simple rules for indices which must be understood:

First rule: To multiply together powers of a quantity, add the indices. To divide, subtract the index of the divisor from the index of the dividend.

Example: Multiply $a \times a^2 \times a^4$ (a means a^1, but the index 1 is always omitted).

$$a \times a^2 \times a^4 = a^{1+2+4} = a^7.$$

Divide a^6 by a^2.

$$\frac{a^6}{a^2} = a^{6-2} = a^4.$$

The student will, we hope, recognise the connection between these examples and the method of working of the slide rule.

Problem 25. Multiply $a^{\frac{3}{4}} \times a^3 \times a^{-\frac{1}{2}}$.

Divide $a^{\frac{1}{4}}$ by a^2.

Second rule: To calculate the power of a power of a quantity, multiply the two indices together.

Example: $(b^3)^2 = b^6$.

$$(b^4)^{-\frac{1}{2}} = b^{-2} = \frac{1}{b^2}.$$

Third rule: To raise to any power, a quantity which consists of several factors, raise each factor to the given power.

Example: Raise $a^2 b m^{\frac{1}{2}} n^{-3}$ to the 5th power.

$$(a^2 b m^{\frac{1}{2}} n^{-3})^5 = a^{10} b^5 m^{\frac{5}{2}} n^{-15}.$$

Problem 26. Reduce to a simple form: $(x^{-\frac{1}{4}} y^{-\frac{1}{2}})^{-8} xy^{-4}$.

Logarithms

By using logarithms we can often calculate much more rapidly than by ordinary arithmetic. There are some calculations which may readily be made with the aid of logs which would be almost impossible otherwise. The slide rule is the mechanical method of computing by logs.

A logarithm is a number. It is the power to which one quantity must be raised to make it equal to another quantity.

For instance, if $a^b = N$, then we might say that the quantity a (called the base) must be raised to the power b in order to be equal to the quantity N, or, expressed in the orthodox manner, b is the logarithm of N to the base a.

Example: $5^3 = 125$, therefore the log of 125 to the base 5 is 3.

Problem 27. What is the log of 32 to base 2?

There is a system of logarithms termed Naperian—after the inventor of logarithms—or natural or hyperbolic logarithms, which has as base the number 2·7183, always denoted by e. This system of logs is of great importance in some parts of mathematics; it is never used for ordinary calculations such as we are concerned with, and the reader need not be in the least concerned with it at present; a brief reference to it was made in Section 6.

In all our numerical work we use a system of logarithms to base 10, generally called common logarithms. In the following notes we shall be dealing with common logs to the base 10 exclusively:

$$10 = 10^1 \quad \therefore \ \log 10 = 1.$$
$$100 = 10^2 \quad \therefore \ \log 100 = 2.$$
$$10,000 = 10^4 \quad \therefore \ \log 10,000 = 4.$$
$$1,000,000 = 10^6 \quad \therefore \ \log 1,000,000 = 6.$$

Multiplication and Division

To multiply together 100 and 10,000 we might apparently take the log of 100, which is 2, the log of 10,000, which is 4, and add them together, $2 + 4 = 6$. If we now look for the number whose log is 6, we see it is 1,000,000, which is the product of $100 \times 10,000$.

From the foregoing example we deduce the simple rule that the log of a product is the sum of the logs of the individual factors.

The reader will see that we have merely used the first index rule mentioned a little earlier in this section, and he will no doubt be able to anticipate the rule for division, which is: The log of the quotient is obtained by subtracting the log of the divisor from the log of the dividend.

If we divide $10,000 \div 1000$ mentally, we obtain 10 as the result. The log of 10,000 is 4, the log of 1000 is 3, and the difference between these two logs is 1, which is the log of 10. Our rule for division gives a correct result.

So far we have dealt only with numbers which are integral powers of 10. We can write down the logs of all such numbers by noticing that the log is the number of noughts following the 1. Between 10 and 100 there are 90 whole numbers, 11, 12, 13—97, 98, 99, and it is clear that if we desire to use a number say, 43, as a factor of multiplication or division we must be able to write down its logarithm: 43 lies between 10 and 100 and its log must lie between 1 and 2, since $\log 10 = 1$ and $\log 100 = 2$. Tables of logarithms have been calculated for our use. There are four-figure logs, in which the decimal part is given to four places of decimals, and these are sufficiently accurate for many purposes, and the whole range of figures is printed on four pages of this book. For more accurate work there are five-figure and seven-figure logs; the latter would fill perhaps 200 pages of this book and cannot, of course, be given They require a book to themselves and are to be found in books of Mathematical Tables, which are devoted to logs and other tables.

If we consult the table on page 156 and run our eye down the first column of figures, we find 43 a few lines from the bottom. In the second column we find the figures 6335. This is the decimal part of the log of 43, and it is called the mantissa of the log. Now we know that the log of 43 lies between 1 and 2, and with the aid of the table we can now write it down; it is 1·6335. The integer, or whole number part of the log—the 1 in this case—is termed the characteristic of the logarithm. The characteristic is always one less than the number of integers which precede the decimal point in the number whose log we are seeking.

We will write down one further log for practice, but this part of the work is so easy that we need not pause long at this stage.

Write down the log of 876·4. On page 157 we find 87 in the first column of figures, and place our pencil over it. Now we move the pencil horizontally to the right until it reaches the column of figures which has 6 in its top line—this is the eighth column from the left. The number we find at this point is 9425. Keeping this number marked with a finger of the left hand, we carry the pencil still further to the right until it reaches the column headed 4 in the differences section of the table on the right; it is the sixth column from the right-hand side of the table. In this column we find the number 2; we have now marked with the left hand the number 9425, and with the pencil the number 2. Adding these together we obtain 9427 as the mantissa of the log we are seeking.

There are three figures before the decimal point of our number 876·4, so that characteristic of the log is 2.

Log 876·4 is 2·9427.

In the top part of the table on page 156 you will notice that opposite numbers 10 to 19 in the left-hand column there are two series of figures in the columns of differences on the right. At this part of the table the mantissae alter rather quickly, and the differences have to be changed. Notice that the figures in the main part of the table step down after the column headed 5. Now, if you are using figures in the main part of the table in columns 0 to 4, which are printed high, you must use the upper figures in the difference columns. From column 5 to column 9 in the main table, the figures are printed lower; if you are using any of these you must also use the lower line of figures in the differences columns.

Problem 28. Write down the logs of the following numbers: 10, 110, 21·6, 942·3 and 1865.

The log of 1 is 0.

We can see that this must be so because $1 = \dfrac{10^1}{10^1} = 10^{1-1}$ $= 10^0$, a result which follows from the first index rule. The reader will see that the result will be the same if we took any power of any quantity and divided it by itself, e.g. $1 = \dfrac{a^n}{a^n}$ $= a^{n-n} = a^0$. If log 1 had some value other than nothing, the reader will see that our logarithmic rule for multiplication would be invalid. The logs of numbers between 1 and 10 lie between 0 and 1.

Example: Using logs, compute the value of $18·63 \times 7·644$.

From the table log $18·63 = 1·2702$
  log $7·644 = ·8833$

Adding $2·1535$

2·1535 is the log of 142·4, the result.

Looking in the table for the number whose log is 2·1535, we first ignore the characteristic 2 and find the decimal part ·1535. Opposite 14 in the first column and under the 2 in the top line we find 1523. The difference of 12 is found in the column of differences headed 4. The number whose log we are seeking is 142·4; the position of the decimal point is governed by the characteristic 2.

On pages 158-9 will be found tables of figures called anti-logarithms. While it is quite easy to find a number corresponding to a given logarithm by using the table of logs, it is just a little easier to use the table of antilogs. Using only the mantissa of the log and the same method as when looking out a logarithm, the reader will have no difficulty in finding the number 1424 corresponding to the mantissa 1535.

Problem 29. Using logs, evaluate $124 \cdot 0 \times 50 \cdot 63 \times 1 \cdot 2 \times 8 \cdot 69$.

Example: Using logs, evaluate $\dfrac{4299}{67}$.

$$\text{Log } 4299 = 3 \cdot 6334$$
$$67 = 1 \cdot 8261$$

Difference $\qquad 1 \cdot 8073$
Antilog $1 \cdot 8073 \quad = 64 \cdot 16$.

Problem 30. Using logs, evaluate $\dfrac{18 \cdot 92 \times 104 \times 7 \cdot 22}{50 \cdot 18 \times 19 \cdot 6}$.

Powers and Roots

We could, if necessary, find the value of $1 \cdot 63^{18}$ by direct multiplication, but we should feel aggrieved if the necessity arose. We should probably proceed to cube $1 \cdot 63$, then cube the result so obtained and then square, i.e. find $[(1 \cdot 63^3)^3]^2$.

Working to only four places of decimals throughout, the work would take half an hour with a chance of making a slip.

Observe the work involved when using logs.

$$\text{Log } 1 \cdot 63 = \cdot 2122$$

(multiply by 18) $\quad 18$

$$\begin{array}{r} 2122 \\ 16976 \\ \hline 3 \cdot 8196 \end{array}$$

Antilog $3 \cdot 8196 = 6601$ Result.

If we had to find the eighteenth root of $1 \cdot 63$ the calculation would be just as simple. Dividing $\cdot 2122$ by 18 we obtain $\cdot 0118$, which is the antilog of $1 \cdot 028$. $\therefore \sqrt[18]{1 \cdot 63} = 1 \cdot 028$.

The reader will notice that we might have selected a much higher power or root than 18 as our example, and the work of multiplying by ordinary methods might then become impossible. We leave the reader to speculate on the other difficulties of extracting the root.

We can imagine the reader objecting that the evaluation of high powers or roots is never a practical necessity. Calculation of compound interest over long periods is just such a problem however. Now let us evaluate what at first sight appears to be a simple quantity, such as $2^{1\cdot41}$, which is of practical importance in problems concerning internal-combustion engines. The reader will quickly discover that, without the aid of logs or slide rule, he is faced with a real difficulty. The ease with which powers and roots of numbers can be calculated with logs is perhaps the most valuable property of this branch of mathematics.

Example: Evaluate $2^{1\cdot41}$ and $^{1\cdot41}\sqrt{2}$.

Log $2 = \cdot3010$. $\cdot3010 \div 1\cdot41 = \cdot2135$.

$\cdot3010 \times 1\cdot41 = \cdot4244$.   Antilog $\cdot2135 = 1\cdot635$.

Antilog $\cdot4244 = 2\cdot657$.

Problem 31. Evaluate $8\cdot7^{5\cdot2}$ and $^5\sqrt{243}$.

Logarithms with Negative Characteristics

We hope that up to this stage any reader hitherto unacquainted with logs has been able to follow these notes without much difficulty. The remainder of this section is, perhaps, a little more complex, and if the reader feels that he is getting out of his depth we recommend him to stop at this stage for a time. If he works more examples of a simple type—which he can easily make up for himself—the pause will give time for the knowledge he has absorbed to sink in, and he will find that the difficulties diminish.

Ability to work with logs is a great asset. Some of the simple examples and problems we have earlier examined could not have been worked out by other means, except a slide rule, which we now know is the quick and easy way of using logs. It may be that the reader is taking this section in his stride. If so, he may safely proceed.

We have seen that the log 1 is 0. While numbers increase from 1 to 10, the corresponding logs increase from 0 to 1. By the time the number has reached 100, the log has grown to 2. It is quite clear that the logs do not increase at a steady rate, by which we mean that the difference between the logs, say of 10 and 20, is not the same as the difference between logs of 20 and 30, or 80 and 90. It is because of this variable rate of increase that we see the divisions crowd together more and more as we look along the scales of our slide rule.

Now we must learn something of the logarithms of numbers less than unity. Take a simple fraction, say ·5. Use the fraction $\frac{1}{2}$ and proceed to divide 2 into 1 using logs.

Log $1 = 0$ and log $2 = ·3010$ $\therefore$ log $\frac{1}{2} = 0 - ·3010$. If to $-·3010$ we add 1 and subtract 1 we shall not alter the value. $-1 + (1 - ·3010)$ gives $-1 + ·699$.

If we consult our table of logs we find the log of 5 is ·6990; we know also that the log of 50 is 1·6990, and of 500, 2·6990, and now we find the log of ·5 is $-1 + ·6990$. This number is usually written $\bar{1}·6990$, and expressed in words by "Bar 1 point 6990". The reader should have no difficulty in showing that log ·05, which is $\frac{1}{20}$, is $\bar{2}·6990$, and the log of ·005 is $\bar{3}·6990$. The bar denotes that the characteristic is negative while the mantissa remains positive. By adopting this method of expressing the values of logs of numbers less than 1, we need only one table of logs and antilogs.

The rule for finding in the tables the log of a fraction is quite simple. Express the fraction in its decimal form and find in the table the mantissa of the log of the significant figures. Write the mantissa down with the decimal point immediately preceding it. There is always a negative characteristic for the log of a number less than 1. This negative characteristic is always one greater than the number of noughts which lie between the decimal point and the first significant figure in the number whose log we are seeking. In ·005 there are two noughts between the decimal point and the 5. The characteristic is $\overline{3}$. Similarly, for ·05 the characteristic is $\overline{2}$. The reader will see that the rule also applies to ·5, the characteristic being $\overline{1}$.

The following table may help at this stage:

Number	Logarithm
$5000 = 5 \times 10^3$	$·6990 + 3 = 3·6990$
$500 = 5 \times 10^2$	$·6990 + 2 = 2·6990$
$50 = 5 \times 10^1$	$·6990 + 1 = 1·6990$
$5 = 5 \times 10^2$	$·6990 + 0 = ·6990$
$·5 = 5 \times 10^{-1}$	$·6990 - \overline{1} = 1·6990$
$·05 = 5 \times 10^{-2}$	$·6990 - \overline{2} = 2·6690$
$·005 = 5 \times 10^{-3}$	$·6990 - \overline{3} = 3·6990$

Example: Using the log tables, write down the logs of ·0123 and ·006009. From the tables we see the log of 123 is 0899, and of 6009 is 7788.

The required logs are $\overline{2}·0899$ and $\overline{3}·7788$.

Problem 32. Using the tables, find the logs of ·802 and ·001176. Also find the numbers whose logs are $\overline{1}·6261$ and $\overline{3}·4710$.

We will end this section with two examples which involve negative characteristics.

Example: Find the square root of ·00591.

$$\sqrt{·00591} = (·00591)^{\frac{1}{2}}$$
$$\text{Log } ·00591 = \overline{3}·7716.$$

We must divide the log by 2 and to do this we increase the negative part by 1 to make it exactly divisible by 2, and to maintain the log unaltered we must also increase the positive part by 1.

We then have $\overline{4} + 1 \cdot 7716$, and this divided by 2 is $\overline{2} + \cdot 8858$ or $\overline{2} \cdot 8858$.

Antilog $2 \cdot 8858 = \cdot 07688$.

The square root of $\cdot 00591$ is $\pm \cdot 07688$.

The $\pm$ sign indicates that the root may be either positive or negative.

Example: Using logs, evaluate $\dfrac{5 \cdot 722 \times \sqrt[5]{72 \cdot 6}}{(\cdot 0122)^{1 \cdot 2} \times \sqrt{82 \cdot 8}}$.

Log $5 \cdot 722$	$= \cdot 7576$	$\cdot 7576$
$\frac{1}{5}$ log $72 \cdot 6$	$= \frac{1}{5} \times 1 \cdot 8609$	$\cdot 3722$

$\qquad\qquad\qquad\qquad$ Adding $\qquad\qquad$ $1 \cdot 1298$ (1)

$1 \cdot 2$ log $\cdot 0122$	$= 1 \cdot 2 \times \overline{2} \cdot 0864$	
	$= -2 \cdot 4 + \cdot 1037$	
	$= -2 \cdot 2963$	
	$= \overline{3} \cdot 7037$	$\overline{3} \cdot 7037$
$\frac{1}{2}$ log $82 \cdot 8$	$= \frac{1}{2} \times 1 \cdot 918$	$\cdot 9590$

$\qquad\qquad\qquad\qquad$ Adding $\qquad\qquad$ $\overline{2} \cdot 6627$ (2)

$\qquad$ Subtracting (2) from (1) $\quad 2 \cdot 4671$

$\qquad$ Antilog $2 \cdot 4671 = 293 \cdot 2$.

Problem 33. Find the values of

$$\frac{29 \cdot 2 \times \cdot 0826}{\cdot 1945} \text{ and } \frac{\sqrt[3]{1 \cdot 82} + \sqrt{\cdot 0043}}{\sqrt[4]{\cdot 0986} + \sqrt[5]{186 \cdot 9}} \text{ using logs.}$$

We suggest the reader now works through the examples and problems in this section using his slide rule. It will be necessary to use the log-log scale, and we think the task will prove both interesting and valuable.

LOGARITHMS
AND
ANTILOGARITHMS

	0	1	2	3	4	5	6	7	8	9
10	0000	0043	0086	0128	0170	0212	0253	0294	0334	0374
11	0414	0453	0492	0531	0569	0607	0645	0682	0719	0755
12	0792	0828	0864	0899	0934	0969	1004	1038	1072	1106
13	1139	1173	1206	1239	1271	1303	1335	1367	1399	1430
14	1461	1492	1523	1553	1584	1614	1644	1673	1703	1732
15	1761	1790	1818	1847	1875	1903	1931	1959	1987	2014
16	2041	2068	2095	2122	2148	2175	2201	2227	2253	2279
17	2304	2330	2355	2380	2405	2430	2455	2480	2504	2529
18	2553	2577	2601	2625	2648	2672	2695	2718	2742	2765
19	2788	2810	2833	2856	2878	2900	2923	2945	2967	2989
20	3010	3032	3054	3075	3096	3118	3139	3160	3181	3201
21	3222	3243	3263	3284	3304	3324	3345	3365	3385	3404
22	3424	3444	3464	3483	3502	3522	3541	3560	3579	3598
23	3617	3636	3655	3674	3692	3711	3729	3747	3766	3784
24	3802	3820	3838	3856	3874	3892	3909	3927	3945	3962
25	3979	3997	4014	4031	4048	4065	4082	4099	4116	4133
26	4150	4166	4183	4200	4216	4232	4249	4265	4281	4298
27	4314	4330	4346	4362	4378	4393	4409	4425	4440	4456
28	4472	4487	4502	4518	4533	4548	4564	4579	4594	4609
29	4624	4639	4654	4669	4683	4698	4713	4728	4742	4757
30	4771	4786	4800	4814	4829	4843	4857	4871	4886	4900
31	4914	4928	4942	4955	4969	4983	4997	5011	5024	5038
32	5051	5065	5079	5092	5105	5119	5132	5145	5159	5172
33	5185	5198	5211	5224	5237	5250	5263	5276	5289	5302
34	5315	5328	5340	5353	5366	5378	5391	5403	5416	5428
35	5441	5453	5465	5478	5490	5502	5514	5527	5539	5551
36	5563	5575	5587	5599	5611	5623	5635	5647	5658	5670
37	5682	5694	5705	5717	5729	5740	5752	5763	5775	5786
38	5798	5809	5821	5832	5843	5855	5866	5877	5888	5899
39	5911	5922	5933	5944	5955	5966	5977	5988	5999	6010
40	6021	6031	6042	6053	6064	6075	6085	6096	6107	6117
41	6128	6138	6149	6160	6170	6180	6191	6201	6212	6222
42	6232	6243	6253	6263	6274	6284	6294	6304	6314	6325
43	6335	6345	6355	6365	6375	6385	6395	6405	6415	6425
44	6435	6444	6454	6464	6474	6484	6493	6503	6513	6522
45	6532	6542	6551	6561	6571	6580	6590	6599	6609	6618
46	6628	6637	6646	6656	6665	6675	6684	6693	6702	6712
47	6721	6730	6739	6749	6758	6767	6776	6785	6794	6803
48	6812	6821	6830	6839	6848	6857	6866	6875	6884	6893
49	6902	6911	6920	6928	6937	6946	6955	6964	6972	6981

Proportional parts (difference columns, headed 1 2 3 | 4 5 6 | 7 8):

Rows 10–14:
```
4 9 13   17 21 26   30 34
4 8 12   16 20 24   28 32
4 8 12   15 19 23   27 31
4 7 11   15 19 22   26 30
3 7 11   14 18 21   25 28
3 7 10   14 17 20   24 27
3 7 10   13 16 20   23 26
3 6 9    12 15 19   22 25
3 6 9    12 15 17   20 23
```

Rows 15–19:
```
3 6 9    11 14 17   20 23
3 6 8    11 14 17   19 22
3 5 8    11 14 16   19 22
3 5 8    10 13 16   18 21
3 5 8    10 13 15   18 20
2 5 7    10 12 15   17 20
2 5 7    9 12 14    16 19
2 5 7    9 11 14    16 18
2 4 7    9 11 13    16 18
2 4 6    8 11 13    15 17
```

	1	2	3	4	5	6	7	8
20	2	4	6	8	11	13	15	17
21	2	4	6	8	10	12	14	16
22	2	4	6	8	10	12	14	15
23	2	4	6	7	9	11	13	15
24	2	4	5	7	9	11	12	14
25	2	3	5	7	9	10	12	14
26	2	3	5	7	8	10	11	13
27	2	3	5	6	8	9	11	13
28	2	3	5	6	8	9	11	12
29	1	3	4	6	7	9	10	12
30	1	3	4	6	7	9	10	11
31	1	3	4	6	7	8	10	11
32	1	3	4	5	7	8	9	11
33	1	3	4	5	6	8	9	10
34	1	3	4	5	6	8	9	10
35	1	2	4	5	6	7	9	10
36	1	2	4	5	6	7	8	10
37	1	2	3	5	6	7	8	9
38	1	2	3	5	6	7	8	9
39	1	2	3	4	5	7	8	9
40	1	2	3	4	5	6	8	9
41	1	2	3	4	5	6	7	8
42	1	2	3	4	5	6	7	8
43	1	2	3	4	5	6	7	8
44	1	2	3	4	5	6	7	8
45	1	2	3	4	5	6	7	8
46	1	2	3	4	5	6	7	7
47	1	2	3	4	5	5	6	7
48	1	2	3	4	4	5	6	7
49	1	2	3	4	4	5	6	7

0	1	2	3	4	5	6	7	8	9	1	2	3	4	5	6	7	8	9
6990	6998	7007	7016	7024	7033	7042	7050	7059	7067	1	2	3	3	4	5	6	7	8
7076	7084	7093	7101	7119	7118	7126	7135	7143	7152	1	2	3	3	4	5	6	7	8
7160	7168	7177	7185	7193	7202	7210	7218	7226	7235	1	2	2	3	4	5	6	7	7
7243	7251	7259	7267	7275	7284	7292	7300	7308	7316	1	2	2	3	4	5	6	6	7
7324	7332	7340	7348	7356	7364	7372	7380	7388	7396	1	2	2	3	4	5	6	6	7
7404	7412	7419	7427	7435	7443	7451	7459	7466	7474	1	2	2	3	4	5	5	6	7
7482	7490	7497	7505	7513	7520	7528	7536	7543	7551	1	2	2	3	4	5	5	6	7
7559	7566	7574	7582	7589	7597	7604	7612	7619	7627	1	2	2	3	4	5	5	6	7
7634	7642	7649	7657	7664	7672	7679	7686	7694	7701	1	1	2	3	4	4	5	6	7
7709	7716	7723	7731	7738	7745	7752	7760	7767	7774	1	1	2	3	4	4	5	6	7
7782	7789	7796	7803	7810	7818	7825	7832	7839	7846	1	1	2	3	4	4	5	6	6
7853	7860	7868	7875	7882	7889	7896	7903	7910	7917	1	1	2	3	4	4	5	6	6
7924	7931	7938	7945	7952	7959	7966	7973	7980	7987	1	1	2	3	3	4	5	6	6
7993	8000	8007	8014	8021	8028	8035	8041	8048	8055	1	1	2	3	4	5	5	5	6
8062	8069	8075	8082	8089	8096	8102	8109	8116	8122	1	1	2	3	3	4	5	5	6
8129	8136	8142	8149	8156	8162	8169	8176	8182	8189	1	1	2	3	4	4	5	5	6
8195	8202	8209	8215	8222	8228	8235	8241	8248	8254	1	1	2	3	4	4	5	5	6
8261	8267	8274	8280	8287	8293	8299	8306	8312	8319	1	1	2	3	4	4	5	5	6
8325	8331	8338	8344	8351	8357	8363	8370	8376	8382	1	1	2	3	3	4	4	5	6
8388	8395	8401	8407	8414	8420	8426	8432	8439	8445	1	1	2	2	3	4	4	5	6
8451	8457	8463	8470	8476	8482	8488	8494	8500	8506	1	1	2	2	3	4	4	5	6
8513	8519	8525	8531	8537	8543	8549	8555	8561	8567	1	1	2	2	3	4	4	5	5
8573	8579	8585	8591	8597	8603	8609	8615	8621	8627	1	1	2	2	3	4	4	5	5
8633	8639	8645	8651	8657	8663	8669	8675	8681	8686	1	1	2	2	3	4	4	5	5
8692	8698	8704	8710	8716	8722	8727	8733	8739	8745	1	1	2	2	3	4	4	5	5
8751	8756	8762	8768	8774	8779	8785	8791	8797	8802	1	1	2	2	3	3	4	5	5
8808	8814	8820	8825	8831	8837	8842	8848	8854	8859	1	1	2	2	3	3	4	5	5
8865	8871	8876	8882	8887	8893	8899	8904	8910	8915	1	1	2	2	3	3	4	4	5
8921	8927	8932	8938	8943	8949	8954	8960	8965	8971	1	1	2	2	3	3	4	4	5
8976	8982	8987	8993	8998	9004	9009	9015	9020	9025	1	1	2	2	3	3	4	4	5
9031	9036	9042	9047	9053	9058	9063	9069	9074	9079	1	1	2	2	3	3	4	4	5
9085	9090	9096	9101	9106	9112	9117	9122	9128	9133	1	1	2	2	3	3	4	4	5
9138	9143	9149	9154	9159	9165	9170	9175	9180	9186	1	1	2	2	3	3	4	4	5
9191	9196	9201	9206	9212	9217	9222	9227	9232	9238	1	1	2	2	3	3	4	4	5
9243	9248	9253	9258	9263	9269	9274	9279	9284	9289	1	1	2	2	3	3	4	4	5
9294	9299	9304	9309	9315	9320	9325	9330	9335	9340	1	1	2	2	3	3	4	4	5
9345	9350	9355	9360	9365	9370	9375	9380	9385	9390	1	1	2	2	3	3	4	4	5
9395	9400	9405	9410	9415	9420	9425	9430	9435	9440	0	1	1	2	2	3	3	4	4
9445	9450	9455	9460	9465	9469	9474	9479	9484	9489	0	1	1	2	2	3	3	4	4
9494	9499	9504	9509	9513	9518	9523	9528	9533	9538	0	1	1	2	2	3	3	4	4
9542	9547	9552	9557	9562	9566	9571	9576	9581	9586	0	1	1	2	2	3	3	4	4
9590	9595	9600	9605	9609	9614	9619	9624	9628	9633	0	1	1	2	2	3	3	4	4
9638	9643	9647	9652	9657	9661	9666	9671	9675	9680	0	1	1	2	2	3	3	4	4
9685	9689	9694	9699	9703	9708	9713	9717	9722	9727	0	1	1	2	2	3	3	4	4
9731	9736	9741	9745	9750	9754	9759	9763	9768	9773	0	1	1	2	2	3	3	4	4
9777	9782	9786	9791	9795	9800	9805	9809	9814	9818	0	1	1	2	2	3	3	4	4
9823	9827	9832	9836	9841	9845	9850	9854	9859	9863	0	1	1	2	2	3	3	4	4
9868	9872	9877	9881	9886	9890	9894	9899	9903	9908	0	1	1	2	2	3	3	4	4
9912	9917	9921	9926	9930	9934	9939	9943	9948	9952	0	1	1	2	2	3	3	4	4
9956	9961	9965	9969	9974	9978	9983	9987	9991	9996	0	1	1	2	2	3	3	3	4

	0	1	2	3	4	5	6	7	8	9	1	2	3	4	5	6	7
·00	1000	1002	1005	1007	1009	1012	1014	1016	1019	1021	0	0	1	1	1	1	2
·01	1023	1026	1028	1030	1033	1035	1038	1040	1042	1045	0	0	1	1	1	1	2
·02	1047	1050	1052	1054	1057	1059	1062	1064	1067	1069	0	0	1	1	1	1	2
·03	1072	1074	1076	1079	1081	1084	1086	1089	1091	1094	0	0	1	1	1	1	2
·04	1096	1099	1102	1104	1107	1109	1112	1114	1117	1119	0	1	1	1	1	2	2
·05	1122	1125	1127	1130	1132	1135	1138	1140	1143	1146	0	1	1	1	1	2	2
·06	1148	1151	1153	1156	1159	1161	1164	1167	1169	1172	0	1	1	1	1	2	2
·07	1175	1178	1180	1183	1186	1189	1191	1194	1197	1199	0	1	1	1	1	2	2
·08	1202	1205	1208	1211	1213	1216	1219	1222	1225	1227	0	1	1	1	1	2	2
·09	1230	1233	1236	1239	1242	1245	1247	1250	1253	1256	0	1	1	1	1	2	2
·10	1259	1262	1265	1268	1271	1274	1276	1279	1282	1285	0	1	1	1	1	2	2
·11	1288	1291	1294	1297	1300	1303	1306	1309	1312	1315	0	1	1	1	2	2	2
·12	1318	1321	1324	1327	1330	1334	1337	1340	1343	1346	0	1	1	1	2	2	2
·13	1349	1352	1355	1358	1361	1365	1368	1371	1374	1377	0	1	1	1	2	2	2
·14	1380	1384	1387	1390	1393	1396	1400	1403	1406	1409	0	1	1	1	2	2	2
·15	1413	1416	1419	1422	1426	1429	1432	1435	1439	1442	0	1	1	1	2	2	2
·16	1445	1449	1452	1455	1459	1462	1466	1469	1472	1476	0	1	1	1	2	2	2
·17	1479	1483	1486	1489	1493	1496	1500	1503	1507	1510	0	1	1	1	2	2	2
·18	1514	1517	1521	1524	1528	1531	1535	1538	1542	1545	0	1	1	1	2	2	2
·19	1549	1552	1556	1560	1563	1567	1570	1574	1578	1581	0	1	1	1	2	2	3
·20	1585	1589	1592	1596	1600	1603	1607	1611	1614	1618	0	1	1	1	2	2	3
·21	1622	1626	1629	1633	1637	1641	1644	1648	1652	1656	0	1	1	2	2	2	3
·22	1660	1663	1667	1671	1675	1679	1683	1687	1690	1694	0	1	1	2	2	2	3
·23	1698	1702	1706	1710	1714	1718	1722	1726	1730	1734	0	1	1	2	2	2	3
·24	1738	1742	1746	1750	1754	1758	1762	1766	1770	1774	0	1	1	2	2	2	3
·25	1778	1782	1786	1791	1795	1799	1803	1807	1811	1816	0	1	1	2	2	2	3
·26	1820	1824	1828	1832	1837	1841	1845	1849	1854	1858	0	1	1	2	2	3	3
·27	1862	1866	1871	1875	1879	1884	1888	1892	1897	1901	0	1	1	2	2	3	3
·28	1905	1910	1914	1919	1923	1928	1932	1936	1941	1945	0	1	1	2	2	3	3
·29	1950	1954	1959	1963	1968	1972	1977	1982	1986	1991	0	1	1	2	2	3	3
·30	1995	2000	2004	2009	2014	2018	2023	2028	2032	2037	0	1	1	2	2	3	3
·31	2042	2046	2051	2056	2061	2065	2070	2075	2080	2084	0	1	1	2	2	3	3
·32	2089	2094	2099	2104	2109	2113	2118	2123	2128	2133	0	1	1	2	2	3	3
·33	2138	2143	2148	2153	2158	2163	2168	2173	2178	2183	0	1	1	2	2	3	3
·34	2188	2193	2198	2203	2208	2213	2218	2223	2228	2234	1	1	2	2	3	3	4
·35	2239	2244	2249	2254	2259	2265	2270	2275	2280	2286	1	1	2	2	3	3	4
·36	2291	2296	2301	2307	2312	2317	2323	2328	2333	2339	1	1	2	2	3	3	4
·37	2344	2350	2355	2360	2366	2371	2377	2382	2388	2393	1	1	2	2	3	3	4
·38	2399	2404	2410	2415	2421	2427	2432	2438	2443	2449	1	1	2	2	3	3	4
·39	2455	2460	2466	2472	2477	2483	2489	2495	2500	2506	1	1	2	2	3	3	4
·40	2512	2518	2523	2529	2535	2541	2547	2553	2559	2564	1	1	2	2	3	4	4
·41	2570	2576	2582	2588	2594	2600	2606	2612	2618	2624	1	1	2	2	3	4	4
·42	2630	2636	2642	2649	2655	2661	2667	2673	2679	2685	1	1	2	3	3	4	4
·43	2692	2698	2704	2710	2716	2723	2729	2735	2742	2748	1	1	2	3	3	4	4
·44	2754	2761	2767	2773	2780	2786	2793	2799	2805	2812	1	1	2	3	3	4	4
·45	2818	2825	2831	2838	2844	2851	2858	2864	2871	2877	1	1	2	3	3	4	5
·46	2884	2891	2897	2904	2911	2917	2924	2931	2938	2944	1	1	2	3	3	4	5
·47	2951	2958	2965	2972	2979	2985	2992	2999	3006	3013	1	1	2	3	3	4	5
·48	3020	3027	3034	3041	3048	3055	3062	3069	3076	3083	1	1	2	3	4	4	5
·49	3090	3097	3105	3112	3119	3126	3133	3141	3148	3155	1	1	2	3	4	4	5

0	1	2	3	4	5	6	7	8	9	1	2	3	4	5	6	7	8	9
3162	3170	3177	3184	3192	3199	3206	3214	3221	3228	1	1	2	3	4	4	5	6	7
3236	3243	3251	3258	3266	3273	3281	3289	3296	3304	1	2	2	3	4	5	5	6	7
3311	3319	3327	3334	3342	3350	3357	3365	3373	3381	1	2	2	3	4	5	5	6	7
3388	3396	3404	3412	3420	3428	3436	3443	3451	3459	1	2	2	3	4	5	6	6	7
3467	3475	3483	3491	3499	3508	3516	3524	3532	3540	1	2	2	3	4	5	6	6	7
3548	3556	3565	3573	3581	3589	3597	3606	3614	3622	1	2	2	3	4	5	6	7	7
3631	3639	3648	3656	3664	3673	3681	3690	3698	3707	1	2	3	3	4	5	6	7	8
3715	3724	3733	3741	3750	3758	3767	3776	3784	3793	1	2	3	3	4	5	6	7	8
3802	3811	3819	3828	3837	3846	3855	3864	3873	3882	1	2	3	4	4	5	6	7	8
3890	3899	3908	3917	3926	3936	3945	8954	3963	3972	1	2	3	4	5	5	6	7	8
3981	3990	3999	4009	4018	4027	4036	4046	4055	4064	1	2	3	4	5	6	6	7	8
4074	4083	4093	4102	4111	4121	4130	4140	4150	4159	1	2	3	4	5	6	7	8	9
4169	4178	4188	4198	4207	4217	4227	4236	4246	4256	1	2	3	4	5	6	7	8	9
4266	4276	4285	4295	4305	4315	4325	4335	4345	4355	1	2	3	4	5	6	7	8	9
4365	4375	4385	4395	4406	4416	4426	4436	4446	4457	1	2	3	4	5	6	7	8	9
4467	4477	4487	4498	4508	4519	4529	4539	4550	4560	1	2	3	4	5	6	7	8	9
4571	4581	4592	4603	4613	4624	4634	4645	4656	4667	1	2	3	4	5	6	7	9	10
4677	4688	4699	4710	4721	4732	4742	4753	4764	4775	1	2	3	4	5	7	8	9	10
4786	4797	4808	4819	4831	4842	4853	4864	4875	4887	1	2	3	4	6	7	8	9	10
4898	4909	4920	4932	4943	4955	4966	4977	4989	5000	1	2	3	5	6	7	8	9	10
5012	5023	5035	5047	5058	5070	5082	5093	5105	5117	1	2	4	5	6	7	8	9	11
5129	5140	5152	5164	5176	5188	5200	5212	5224	5236	1	2	4	5	6	7	8	10	11
5248	5260	5272	5284	5297	5309	5321	5333	5346	5358	1	2	4	5	6	7	9	10	11
5370	5383	5395	5408	5420	5433	5445	5458	5470	5483	1	3	4	5	6	8	9	10	11
5495	5508	5521	5534	5546	5559	5572	5585	5598	5610	1	3	4	5	6	8	9	10	12
5623	5636	5649	5662	5675	5689	5702	5715	5728	5741	1	3	4	5	7	8	9	10	12
5754	5768	5781	5794	5808	5821	5834	5848	5861	5875	1	3	4	5	7	8	9	11	12
5888	5902	5916	5929	5943	5957	5970	5984	5998	6012	1	3	4	5	7	8	10	11	12
6026	6039	6053	6067	6081	6095	6109	6124	6138	6152	1	3	4	6	7	8	10	11	13
6166	6180	6194	6209	6223	6237	6252	6266	6281	6295	1	3	4	6	7	9	10	11	13
6310	6324	6339	6353	6368	6383	6397	6412	6427	6442	1	3	4	6	7	9	10	12	13
6457	6471	6486	6501	6516	6531	6546	6561	6577	6592	2	3	5	6	8	9	11	12	14
6607	6622	6637	6653	6668	6683	6699	6714	6730	6745	2	3	5	6	8	9	11	12	14
6761	6776	6792	6808	6823	6839	6855	6871	6887	6902	2	3	5	6	8	9	11	13	14
6918	6934	6950	6966	6982	6998	7015	7031	7047	7063	2	3	5	6	8	10	11	13	15
7079	7096	7112	7129	7145	7161	7178	7194	7211	7228	2	3	5	7	8	10	12	13	15
7244	7261	7278	7295	7311	7328	7345	7362	7379	7396	2	3	5	7	8	10	12	13	15
7413	7430	7447	7464	7482	7499	7516	7534	7551	7568	2	3	5	7	9	10	12	14	16
7586	7603	7621	7638	7656	7674	7691	7709	7727	7745	2	4	5	7	9	11	12	14	16
7762	7780	7798	7816	7834	7852	7870	7889	7907	7925	2	4	5	7	9	11	13	14	16
7943	7962	7980	7998	8017	8035	8054	8072	8091	8110	2	4	6	7	9	11	13	15	17
8128	8147	8166	8185	8204	8222	8241	8260	8279	8299	2	4	6	8	9	11	13	15	17
8318	8337	8356	8375	8395	8414	8433	8453	8472	8492	2	4	6	8	10	12	14	15	17
8511	8531	8551	8570	8590	8610	8630	8650	8670	8690	2	4	6	8	10	12	14	16	18
8710	8730	8750	8770	8790	8810	8831	8851	8872	8892	2	4	6	8	10	12	14	16	18
8913	8933	8954	8974	8995	9016	9036	9057	9078	9099	2	4	6	8	10	12	15	17	19
9120	9141	9162	9183	9204	9226	9247	9268	9290	9311	2	4	6	8	11	13	15	17	19
9333	9354	9376	9397	9419	9441	9462	9484	9506	9528	2	4	7	9	11	13	15	17	20
9550	9572	9594	9616	9638	9661	9683	9705	9727	9750	2	4	7	9	11	13	16	18	20
9772	9795	9817	9840	9863	9886	9908	9931	9954	9977	2	5	7	9	11	14	16	18	20

OTHER CALCULATING INSTRUMENTS

IN order to accommodate long logarithmic scales, and with a view to securing a higher degree of accuracy, various devices are employed. We cannot proceed with a lengthy description of the instruments which are available; the reader will see them illustrated in catalogues of mathematical instruments, but we will make a short reference to the principles employed.

Cylindrical Calculators

Let us visualise a logarithmic scale in the form of the diagram illustrated in Fig. 43. The graduations commence at A and run

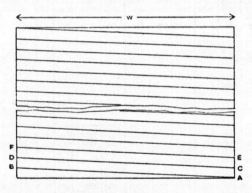

FIG. 43

in a sloping direction to B, continue from C to D, and then from E to F, and so on. B and C are identical points in the scale, as also are D and E. The total length of the scale is the sum of all the sloping lines. This flat scale is glued on to a cylindrical stock whose circumference exactly equals the width W of the rectangle, and the sloping lines now form a continuous helix, the point B joining up with C, D with E, etc.

In some instruments the total length of the scale is 12·5 m, i.e. 50 times the length of scale of a standard slide rule, and the degree of accuracy attainable is high. The instrument is operated by means of adjustable pointers, which may be set to any desired points on the scale and then moved together to other positions. If the reader will take a pair of dividers and set them to, say, the distance between 1 and 3 on the D scale of his slide rule, then move them so that the left-hand leg is placed at 2, the right-hand leg will register with the 6. This is the fundamental method of multiplication of $2 \times 3 = 6$, and in principle it is the method used in the cylindrical calculator employing the helical scale.

In other cylindrical instruments the scale runs in sections in the axial direction, and is used in conjunction with a grid surrounding the main cylinder.

Circular Calculators

The reader will understand that it is easy to set out the C and D scales of his slide rule in circular instead of rectilinear form. Fig. 44 shows, slightly reduced in size, a simple form of circular calculator in which the C and D scales are still 250 mm in length but, being in circular form, result in a more compact instrument.

The reference letters A, B, C, D and E mentioned in the description allude to the five circular scales, taken in order from outer to inner.

Scale E is for evaluating squares and square roots; scale B deals similarly with cubes and cube roots, and the outer scale A gives a means of finding common logarithms. The cursor takes the form of a transparent sector, rotating about the centre, on which is drawn a radial hair line.

Multiplication is effected by rotating a knob at the back of the instrument to bring the 1 of D into coincidence with one of the factors in C; opposite the second factor in D the product will be found in C. These operations are exactly analogous to

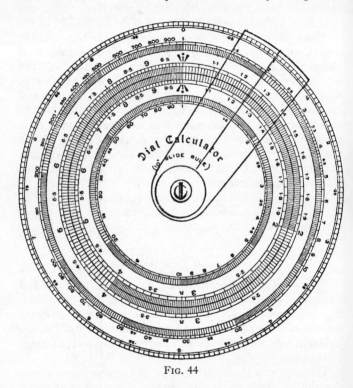

FIG. 44

the movement of the slide of the ordinary slide rule. Division, and combined multiplication and division, follow the same general rules applicable to slide rules. Squares and square roots, cubes and cube roots, and logarithms are found by projecting by means of the rotating cursor from the appropriate scale to the C or D scales, and *vice versa*.

Fig. 45 shows a circular calculator in which the main scale is

1·25 m long. This scale occupies five concentric circles; if the numbering is followed progressively round the five circles starting at 1 in the smallest circle, and proceeding clockwise

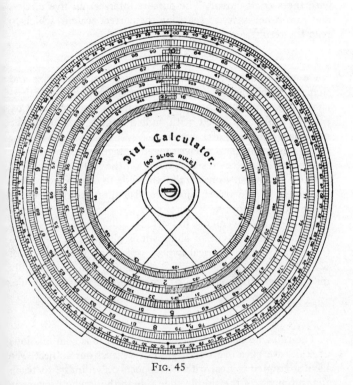

FIG. 45

until the 10 in the fifth circle is reached, no difficulty in passing from one circle to the next will be encountered. Short lengths of bridging scales are provided to assist. The outermost scale is evenly divided and this, in conjunction with the main scale, gives mantissae of common logarithms.

Multiplication is effected by setting the first cursor to the 1 of the main scale and the second cursor to one of the factors in the main scale. By means of a knob at the back of the instrument the two cursors are *moved together* to bring the first cursor to the second factor, and the product appears coincident with the second cursor. The cursors intersect all five circles, and care is necessary in selecting the correct scale in which to read the result.

Watch-type Calculators

Circular calculators resembling pocket watches in size and shape are available. In principle they resemble the two calculators illustrated in Figs. 44 and 45, but they are operated by small spindles equipped with milled heads, similar to the winding mechanism of a watch.

Circulator calculators have one advantage over the ordinary type of slide rule: the result is never off the scale, and there is nothing equivalent to traversing the slide to change over from one index to the other; they are also more convenient for carrying in the pocket.

For general convenience in working, and for speed in operation, the ordinary type of slide rule is altogether superior to the circular or cylindrical types, and when the novelty of working with the latter has worn off the user almost invariably discards the instrument and reverts to the use of his slide rule.

Other Rules

The rules we have described, and the various combinations of scales we have dealt with, do not exhaust our subject. We have attempted to deal with two aspects only: firstly, to teach the rudiments of the simple slide rule to those who previously were unacquainted with them, and to stress the argument that proficiency can be attained easily; secondly, to convince those who use only the standard type of rule that they are employing an instrument of limited utility, and that other rules are available which, whilst retaining the best points of the standard rule, have other features which increase the efficiency of the instrument.

It is quite probable that the reader will occasionally see a slide rule which is equipped with one or more scales which we have not mentioned. As stated above, we do not claim to have completely covered the subject in this small book, but we think we have dealt with the most useful scales. We have made no attempt to deal with the large variety of special slide rules designed for effecting computations related to specific industries. Such slide rules (which are often used for advertising purposes) shorten the work connected with specific problems, but computations effected with their aid may usually be carried out by the ordinary types of slide rule.

HISTORICAL NOTE

NATURAL or hyperbolic logarithms were invented by Napier of Merchiston in 1614, and the system is frequently known by the name of Naperian logarithms. The base of the Naperian system of logs is $2 \cdot 7183$; this number is usually denoted by e. Common logarithms, namely those to the base 10, are sometimes called Briggsian logarithms; this system is invariably used for ordinary computations.

The first practical application of logs in the form of scales was produced by Professor Gunter in 1620. His instrument consisted of one scale only, and was used in conjunction with a pair of dividers. The slide rule in its modern form was first devised by Wingate in 1626, and the cursor was added by Mannheim in 1851.

Degree of Accuracy

The only criticism we hear advanced against the slide rule is that results obtained with its aid are not always exact. Speaking now of the 250 mm C and D scales, errors should not much exceed $\cdot 1$ to $\cdot 2\%$. Accuracy will depend upon the care taken in manipulating and reading, and upon the accuracy of the instrument itself. All slide rules exhibit small errors in the dividing of the scales if examined critically, but in a good instrument such errors are small and often difficult to detect. In the course of time, defects develop due to shrinkage or distortion of the rule itself. An old rule frequently displays discrepancies in the lengths of the scales which originally were identical. The effective life of a rule will be considerably lengthened by careful treatment and protection from unnecessary exposure in a hot or moist atmosphere.

The negligence of the shopkeeper who displays for sale slide rules in his window, in the direct rays of the sun, is reprehensible and indicates ignorance of the merchandise he handles. No slide rule, except the all-metal types which are seldom seen, will retain accuracy and easy movement after prolonged exposure in direct sunlight.

We have attempted to advance the claims of slide rules fitted with duplicate scales, such as the types described in sections 9 and 10. With this type of rule it is possible to obtain results while using much shorter lengths of scales, and, of course, it follows that the errors, due to discrepancies in the scales, will be smaller.

Interpolated readings are certain to introduce small errors in results, since all we can do in assessing values which do not coincide with an actual graduation of the scales is to estimate their position as though the scales are evenly divided instead of being logarithmic. These errors are smaller than perhaps would be expected. The widest space in the C or D scale of the 250 mm rule is that lying between 4 and 4·05. If we set the cursor index exactly in the middle of this space we should no doubt read its position as *4·025*. Its true reading should be 4·0249. We are, however, likely to make larger errors when we estimate other fractions of spaces, since the half-way position is the easiest of all to assess correctly.

All instruments when used are susceptible to errors of varying degrees. If we are asked to name a simple instrument possessing a high degree of accuracy, we immediately think of the engineer's micrometer. In using the instrument, we may, as a result of error in the thread, or zero error, or faulty execution, obtain an error of 10 μm. If we are measuring a rod of about 10 mm diameter, the 10 μm error is of the order of 1 in 1000, not far removed from the degree of error we may encounter in a slide rule. If we are measuring the thickness of a sheet of foil of the order of 100 μm, our micrometer error is 10%, something much worse than our slide rule inaccuracies. Again, a work's accountant might criticise the slide rule because it may not give him quite accurately the cost of 4·3 t of material at £1·26 per tonne, forgetting that his weight may be in error to the extent of 1% or more, a larger error than the slide rule will introduce.

When discussing accuracy of slide rule results, points such as those we have mentioned should be remembered.

Gauge Points

In addition to the scale graduations, a few other lines appear in the majority of slide rules. These additional lines, termed gauge points, represent the positions of factors commonly used in calculations.

In nearly all rules the value of $\pi = 3\cdot14159$ is marked in the principal scales, π being the constant which enters into calculations relating to circles, spheres, etc. $\dfrac{\pi}{4} = \cdot7854$, is sometimes shown by a gauge point, $\dfrac{\pi}{4} d^2$ being the area of a circle of diameter d.

Gauge points, denoted by c and c^1, appear at $1\cdot13$ and $3\cdot57$ respectively in the C scale of many slide rules. The volume of a cylinder is $\dfrac{\pi}{4} d^2 l$; it may be written in the form $\left(\dfrac{d}{\sqrt{\dfrac{4}{\pi}}}\right)^2 l$.

The value of $\sqrt{\dfrac{4}{\pi}}$ is approximately $1\cdot13$. If the gauge point c is set to the value of the diameter of a cylinder on D, the volume of the cylinder may be read on A coincident with the length, l, on B. For some values of d and l, the result will be off the scale when c is set to diameter. In such cases, if c^1 is used, the result will be obtainable.

The gauge point M is seen in scales A and B in some makes of rule. Its virtual value is $\dfrac{1}{\pi} = \cdot3183$. To find in one setting of the slide the area of the curved surfaces of a cylinder, we set M to diameter in A and read over the length in B the area of curved surface in A.

Other gauge points may be found, their inclusion or omission being dependent upon the decision of the manufacturers or designers of the rule. We mention the following, which are the commonest:

ρ' at 3438, and ρ'' at 206255, in scale C, give the numbers of minutes and seconds in a radian respectively. These gauge points may be used for finding the values of trigonometrical functions of small angles. For any small angle, say less than $2°$, the sin and the tan may be taken as identical. If we set the ρ' mark to the graduation in scale D, representing one-tenth of the number of minutes in the angle, the sin or tan may be read in D under the 1C or 10C.

Example: Find the sin or tan of 22′.

Set ρ' to 2·2D. Read sin or tan in D under 10C= ·0064.

If the angle is expressed in seconds, the ρ'' is used in a similar manner.

A third gauge point ρg occasionally may be seen between 6·3 and 6·4 on scale C; this is used in the same way when the angle is expressed in the centesimal system.

If we remember that the sin $1°=$ tan $1°=$ ·0174, we shall have no difficulty in inserting the decimal points in results obtained when using these gauge points.

A gauge point is sometimes placed between division 114 and 116 in scales A and B; this is called the gunner's mark, and is used in certain calculations relating to artillery.

The value of $g=9·81$ m/s², the gravitational acceleration imposed on freely falling bodies near the earth's surface, is occasionally indicated by a gauge point. g is used frequently by engineers in problems concerning dynamics. (Sometimes g is marked at its fps value, 32 ft/s².)

The inclusion of many gauge points in a slide rule is to be

deprecated. The only one we think deserves its place is π and possibly $\dfrac{\pi}{4}$.

If any number enters frequently into our calculations, it is fairly easy to add a gauge point to register its position. The mark should be scribed with a razor blade broken so as to provide a sharp corner, and a square should be used to ensure the line lies at right angles to the length of the rule. It is not quite correct, and we have found a safe method to adopt is first to paste a small piece of paper on the scale and very lightly pencil the mark on the paper. The position of the mark should be very carefully checked and, if necessary, corrected. The mark can now be cut through the paper into the scale, care being exercised to avoid cutting too deeply, the paper removed and a trace of printer's ink rubbed into the cut impression, after which the scale may be polished. If neatly executed, a fine black line will result. Lines registering gauge points should stand slightly off the scales with which they are associated, in order to avoid confusion with the divisions of the scales.

The signs $\dfrac{\text{Quot.}}{+1}$ and $\dfrac{\text{Prod.}}{-1}$ which appear at the left and right-hand ends respectively of certain makes of rules are of little consequence, and we would prefer not to discusss them. They are designed to assist in ascertaining the numbers of digits in a product or quotient. We have, in Section 4, given rules for determination of the position of decimal points, based on the position of slide relative to the stock. We have shown that if, when multiplying, the slide is set so that it protrudes to the right of the stock the number of digits in the product is one less than the sum of digits in the two factors. Another way of expressing the same rule is to say: If, when multiplying, the result lies to the right of the first factor the digits in the product are one less than those of the two factors. The sign $\dfrac{\text{Prod.}}{-1}$ at the right-hand end of the stock is a reminder of the rule when expressed in this manner. The sign $\dfrac{\text{Quot.}}{+1}$ similarly reminds us that the quotient will contain one more digit than the difference between the digits of the dividend and divisor if the result appears to the left of the dividend. When the result in a multiplication lies to the left of the first factor, the number of digits of the product is equal to the sum of the numbers of digits in the two factors, and in division the number of digits in the quotient is equal to the difference between the digits of dividend and divisor when the result is found on the right of the dividend.

EXERCISES

We hope that we have given some indication of the number of ways in which a slide rule may be used. It is suitable for use in any work which involves multiplication. In this section we give a number of examples, which include warnings of the sort of error that you are liable to make when using a slide rule, as well as a large number of exercises for you to work on.

One problem, once it has been reduced to the multiplication stage, is very much like another. The only way to become proficient with a slide rule is to understand its fundamental principles and to work out simple exercises.

When a practical problem presents itself, the relevant numbers should be written down; figures which cancel out should be eliminated and simple factors combined mentally to reduce the number of operations with the slide rule. However, a special effort should *not* be made to reduce the number of operations—if it was, the point of the slide rule would be lost.

For example, there is no saving in cancelling $\frac{4}{6}$ to $\times 34 \cdot 2$

$\frac{2}{3} \times 34 \cdot 2$, although there may be some in reducing $\frac{4}{6}$ to $\frac{1}{1 \cdot 5}$.

As a general rule, only make those cancellations and combinations which do make a reduction in work with the rule *and* are immediately obvious to you.

In some of the examples which follow, the rule best suited for use is mentioned. If scales C and D are to be used, any rule will meet the case. If trigonometrical work is involved, use the Darmstadt rule every time; the reader will soon see why we recommend this rule.

The time occupied in making acquaintance with the duplicated C and D scales of Dualistic and Electrical rules will be a good investment.

Now that the British currency has been decimalised, all financial operations are considerably simplified (as was the intention). You should bear the following points in mind:

(1) Answers need only be accurate to three decimal places—or actually two-and-a-half—in any transaction and in most financial transactions the third of these (the $\frac{1}{2}$p) is disregarded.

(2) Take care not to write answers as £7·435, £0·867 or 22·3p, but as £7·43$\frac{1}{2}$, £0·86$\frac{1}{2}$ and 22$\frac{1}{2}$p respectively (unless the $\frac{1}{2}$p is to be disregarded, in which case they will usually be rounded up).

(3) If the accuracy on the rule only allows you to read one decimal place, to write the answer with two (as is required for normal accounting purposes) implies a greater accuracy than is justified. You must make a decision according to the individual merits of the case.

Example: £56·40 is invested at 5$\frac{1}{2}$% per annum compound interest. Calculate the value after 8$\frac{1}{2}$ years.

£1 at the end of one year becomes £$(1 + ·055) =$ 1·055; at the end of two years becomes £$(1·055)$ $(1·055) = $£$(1·055)^2$, and at the end of 8$\frac{1}{2}$ years becomes £$(1·055)^{8\frac{1}{2}}$.

Use log-log scale, and if 1·055 is not within the range of the scale treat as $\dfrac{2·11}{2}$.

Set X to 211LU. 10C to X. X to 85C.

Read in LL under X 570.

Set X to 2LU. 10C to X. X to 85C.

Read in LL under X 360.

Over 57D set 36C.

Under 1C read 1·58D.

Under 564C read 891 in D. £89·10.

Problem 34. The machining of 55 pieces took 440 minutes to complete. The operator's rate of pay was £16 for 40 hours. Calculate the wage cost per piece.

Problem 35. A time sheet for a group of employees shows:
A with $6\frac{1}{2}$ hours overtime at a basic rate of £14·00 for 40 hr. B with $5\frac{3}{4}$ hours overtime at a basic rate of £13.00 for 40 hr. C with $8\frac{1}{4}$ hours overtime at a basic rate of £12.00 for 40 hr. D with 2 hours overtime at a basic rate of £15·20 for 38 hr. E with $11\frac{1}{2}$ hours overtime at a basic rate of £12·25 for 35 hr.

Calculate the overtime payment due at a rate of time and one-third for all overtime.

Problem 36. The price of foil is $11\frac{1}{2}$p per m². Calculate the cost of 100 sheets 530 mm × 395 mm.

As with its money, Britain is gradually replacing its technical and scientific units with a decimal system. In this case the system adopted is the *Système Internationale* (SI), an adaptation of metric units. Again, this will simplify matters considerably. There are possible pitfalls though:

(1) The units as presented may not be in standard form. If all the units are inserted into a problem in standard form, then the answer will drop out in standard form. For example, if there is a problem which gives the question in terms of (metric) tonnes, centimetres and hours and the answer has to be a force, then, if the tonnes, centimetres and hours are converted to kilogrammes, metres and seconds, the answer will automatically be in Newtons. The alternative is not to bother converting until the problem is almost solved. An example is given below.

(2) Any practical problem will not necessarily mention g, the value of gravitational acceleration. This is about 9·81 ms⁻² and would have to be inserted in some problems.

Example: A ship whose mass is 10 Mg, moving with a speed of 5·04 km/h, shuts its engines off. It travels 40 m before coming to rest. What was the average resistance of the water to the passage of the ship?

Basic mechanics gives us that $v^2 - u^2 = 2as$, i.e.

$$a = \frac{v^2 - u^2}{2s}.$$

Also, $F = ma = \dfrac{m(v^2 - u^2)}{2s}.$

Here, $m = 10$ Mg $- 10^4$ kg

$v = 0$

$u = 5·04$ km/h $- \dfrac{5·04 \times 10^3}{3600}$ m/s $- 1·4$ m/s

and $s = 40$ m.

$$\therefore F = \frac{10^4 \times (-(1·4^2))}{2 \times 40}.$$

Of course, this is a fairly easy sum to work out directly, but using the slide rule on the simplified sum $\dfrac{140^2}{80}$ we obtain 245 as the answer. And, because we translated everything into SI to start with, the answer is in the SI unit of force, namely, the Newton. So the answer is 245 N.

Example: A mass of 876 g falls 0·76 m vertically from rest onto the ground. If the mass stops descending 56 cm below ground level, what is the average resistance of the ground to motion?

When the mass has fallen 0·76 m, all its potential energy (given by mgh) is changed to kinetic energy (given by $\frac{1}{2}mv^2$) and so v^2 is equal to $2mgh/m$, i.e. $2gh$.

Using "$v^2 - u^2 = 2as$", $0 - 2gh = 2a$. $0·56$, so $a = -gh/0·56$.

$$F = ma = -mgh/0{\cdot}56 = -\frac{0{\cdot}876 \times 9{\cdot}81 \times 0{\cdot}76}{0{\cdot}56}.$$

$\therefore$ by slide rule, the resistance is $1{\cdot}17$ N.

[In the calculation,
Set 10C to 876D.
Set X to 981C.
Set 56C to X.
Set X to 1C and 10C to X.
Set X to 76C.
Read 117D under 10C.]

Example: A gas has a volume of 188 ml at a pressure of 760 mm of Hg and a temperature of 20° C. What is its volume at 400 mm of Hg and 80° C? What at 625 mm of Hg at a temperature of 65° C? What is the temperature when the gas has a volume of 310 ml at 750 mm of Hg?

The gas laws state that

$$PV = RT$$

where **P** is pressure, **V** is volume, **T** is absolute temperature and **R** is a constant—the gas constant.

Pressure in $N/m^2 \propto$ pressure in mm of Hg. So, if **P** is the pressure in mm of Hg, and **V** is in ml, **T** in °K.

$$PV = R'T$$

$$760 \times 188 = R' \times 293$$

$$R' = \frac{760 \times 188}{293}.$$

Set 10C to 76D, X to 188C.

293C to X.

Read 488D under 10C.

$R' = 488.$

(1) $V = \dfrac{R'T}{P}$

$= \dfrac{\overset{1\cdot22}{\cancel{488}} \times 353}{\underset{1}{\cancel{400}}}$

$= 430$ ml (by slide rule).

(2) $V = \dfrac{R'T}{P}$

$= \dfrac{488 \times 338}{625}$

$= 264$ ml.

[Set 10C to 488D

X to 338C

625C to X.

Read 264D under 10C.]

(3) $T = \dfrac{PV}{R'}$

$= \dfrac{750 \times 310}{488}$

$= 476$ [K]

$= 203°$ C.

These examples may demonstrate, particularly if you do not understand them, that whatever the problem is, if it involves multiplication at any stage, then the slide rule will be able to help you.

It is not the function of a book on the slide rule to teach you how to do every problem that you may come across. The examples could be multiplied indefinitely; but this would serve no useful purpose. The examples that follow are, therefore, either purely numerical or are expressed as simple problems. Even though you are using a slide rule you must be careful not to mix units, not to give answers that are wrong by factors of 10, etc. Once you have reduced the problem in front of you to a multiplication sum which can be handled by the rule, then you proceed as normal.

Do not, however, fall into the trap of using a slide rule when a mental calculation would be quicker. Take warning from the story of the engineer who, when asked what 2×3 was, took out his slide rule and answered "about 6". But the story did go on to relate that when he was asked what $19 \cdot 7\pi$ was he replied "about $61 \cdot 89$"—and in the same time.

In the sums which follow (for that is all they are) you are advised to keep doing them until you feel proficient. Practice is the only way. If your answer does not agree with ours, do it again. If it still does not agree, check it on paper (using tables if necessary). If it *still* does not agree . . . our address is on the back page.

Questions

For each question, reduce the expression given to a single number, not involving constants (such as g and π) or powers (such as 7^4) except of 10 (e.g. 10^7). In answers involving units, the appropriate metric prefix should be used wherever possible.

1. $47\pi \times 9 \cdot 3^3$.

2. $\dfrac{\cdot 0535 \times 74 \cdot 1 \times 4 \cdot 87}{\cdot 1925 \times \cdot 0524}$.

3. $h = 0 \cdot 03 \dfrac{L}{D} \times \dfrac{V^2}{64}$.

   If $h = 0 \cdot 614$, $L = 168$, $D = 0 \cdot 25$, what is V?

4. If $T = 2\pi \sqrt{\dfrac{l}{g}}$, what is T when l is 286 mm?

5. $\dfrac{5 \cdot 28 \times 97 \cdot 6 \times 142}{0 \cdot 034 \times 17 \cdot 7 \times 10^3}$.

6. In a right-angled triangle the two sides (not the hypotenuse) are 160 and 231. What is the angle opposite the short side? What is this in radians?

7. $3 \cdot 5^{2 \cdot 66}$.

8. $(0 \cdot 35)^{2 \cdot 66}$.

9. $(0 \cdot 35)^{0 \cdot 266}$.

10. $x^{2 \cdot 14} = 40$.

11. $(28)^{\frac{3}{4}}$.

12. In an exam the marks scored by the examinees are given below. What are they as percentages of the possible total of 112?
    94 : 96 : 86 : 28 : 47 : 90 : 22 : 74 : 56.

13. If the marks (see question 12) were "scaled", so that the top mark became a score of 100 and the lowest mark became 0, what would each score?

14. $e^{\log 4 \cdot 7 \times 2 \cdot 303}$.

15. $0 \cdot 374 \div 25 \cdot 687$.

ANSWERS TO PROBLEMS

Problem

1. $\frac{49}{60}$.   **2.** $2\frac{3}{5}$.   **3.** $1\frac{1}{10}$.

4. $6\frac{4}{5}$, $13\frac{2}{25}$, $19\frac{2}{25}$, $20\frac{1}{8}$, $41\frac{1}{80}$, $86\frac{5}{8}$.

5. 29·723.   13·593.   **6.** 766·0324.

7. ·875.   ·8125.   **8.** $2\frac{823}{990}$.

9. $e = 1\cdot02$, $f = 1\cdot2$, $g = 2\cdot6$, $h = 2\cdot87$.
$m = 4\cdot05$, $n = 6\cdot25$, $o = 7\cdot72$, $p = 9\cdot075$.

10. £631.   **11.** 2660 m³.   **12.** 71·7%.

13.

Direct Labour	25%
Drawing Office	4%
Materials	31%
Works Overheads	28%
Gen. Office	12%
Total	100%

14. 1·785.

15. ·819. Digits $3 - 3 - (-2) - 2 - 1 + [1] = 0$.

16. 76·7.   27900.

17. 28·5.   90·2.   ·1287.   ·00407.

18. 349 m³.   1986 kg.   **19.** 4740.

20. 2.   4·31.   9·28.   21·2.   ·277.   ·0772.

21. 163.   6·35.   ·00615.

22. 2168000.   1·063.   **23.** 112500.   1·292.

24. 87·5%.   **25.** $a^{\frac{13}{4}}$, $a^{-\frac{3}{2}}$.

26. x^3.   **27.** 5.

28. 1.   2·0414.   1·3345.   2·9742.   3·2706.

29. 65480.   **30.** 14·44.   **31.** 76810.   3.

32. $\bar{1}$·9042. $\bar{3}$·0704.   ·4228.   ·002958.

33. 12·4.   ·378.   **34.** 12p.

35. (*a*) £3·03. (*b*) £2·49. (*c*) £3.30. (*d*) £1·06.
(*e*) £5·36.   **36.** £2·40.

Question

1. $1·19 \times 10^5$.

2. 1914.

3. 1·4.

4. 1·06 s.

5. 121·8.

6. 34·7°; 19·5 radians.

7. 28·0.

8. 0·0612.

9. 0·7563.

10. 5·6.

11. 12·1.

12. 83·9% : 85·6% : 76·7% : 25% : 41·9% : 80·4% : 19·6% :
66% : 50%.

13. 97·2 : 100 : 86·5 : 8·1 : 33·8 : 91·9 : 0 : 70·3 : 45·9.

14. 4·7.

15. 0·01454.

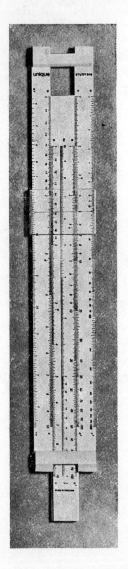

"UNIQUE" SLIDE RULES

FOR EDUCATIONAL, BUSINESS AND HOME USE

The Unique range of slide rules have always provided a high degree of accuracy at a modest cost.

All-plastic and traditional models of hardwood construction are included in the range.

Many scale arrangements are available, from models suitable for an introduction to the slide rule in Junior Schools (J181) to models capable of advanced calculations.

A programme of continuous development is undertaken to advance the design and construction of the slide rule. Special slide rules can be produced to a customer's specification where the requirement would justify development costs.

Unique Slide Rules and other products are exported to all parts of the world. In case of any difficulty in obtaining supplies or information please write direct to us:

Unique Slide Rule Co. Ltd.,
Telscombe Cliffs,
Newhaven,
England

Model illustrated: Unique Study 500, with scales K-A-B-CI-C-D-ST. Code S500.